And The Tigers Come At Night

To Ralph.
I hope you enjoy to read

Basil Jay

authorHOUSE™

1663 Liberty Drive, Suite 200
Bloomington, Indiana 47403
(800) 839-8640
www.AuthorHouse.com

First published by AuthorHouse 08/25/05

ISBN: 1-4208-6636-2 (sc)

Printed in the United States of America
Bloomington, Indiana

This book is printed on acid-free paper.

THE TITLE OF THIS BOOK

AND THE TIGERS COME AT NIGHT

IS TAKEN FROM A LINE IN THE LYRICS OF

I DREAMED A DREAM
BY

Claude-Michel Schonberg
And
Herbert Kretzmer

FROM THE MUSICAL

LES MISERABLES

DEDICATION

To ALL the doctors and nurses
who helped me down
'The Prostate Path' in the summer of 2004
But especially to *'The lovely Nita'*
(she knows who she is) and
the wonderful girls of Winterlands

CONTENTS

CHAPTER 1
A BAD BEGINNING

AUGUST 2004

"Well Mr Jay" he said, "You've got cancer" he said

"Oh" I said

"It's High Grade" he said, "that means it's aggressive" he said

"Oh" I said

"We have a multi-discipline meeting every Monday" He said

"Oh" I said, "I see" I added, anxious to show that I could be as good a conversationalist as the next man, providing of course that the next man wasn't Billy Connelly

"At last weeks meeting you were brought up" he said

Just call me 'vomit', I thought, "Oh" I said

"The meeting was not convinced that the cancer has not already spread to your bones and surrounding tissue" he said

"Oh," then, "Oh dear" I said, stretching my vocabulary

"We have arranged for you to have a full body bone scan, and an MRI scan of the pelvic and abdominal regions" he said

"Oh" I said, then, finding my voice developed the theme "When will that.......?"

"Dr. MacDermot will write to you" he interrupted

"Oh" I said "How soo.......?"

"Dr MacDermot will contact you", he tidied his papers

"Yes, but I wou.........."

"I'm sure Dr McDermot will treat it as priority" he interrupted again

He leaned on his desk and half raised himself, as if to get up.   The consultation was clearly over.

"Thank you" I said, and, climbing down off my chair, I scurried across the floor, crept under the door, and out of his office, a 62 year old man, reduced to less than 2 inches tall by a doctor not long out of short trousers.   I walked numbly along the busy corridor; it was full of people, but I was quite alone.   This wasn't me; I'm not normally 'fobbed' off without having my say.   I can send back a tough steak with the best of them.   But then again, the threat of bone devouring cancer may be tough titty, but it is definitely in a different league to a tough steak.

I walked out of the sombre dark cool of the hospital and into a bright and cheerful day. The sun was shining. But it wasn't shining for me.

It was August 31st 2004.

CHAPTER 2
MY A.R.F.(RITIC) RIGHT FOOT

WINTER 2003/2004

I remember the Queen famously saying in her 1997 Christmas message.

"I have had an *'Annus Horriblias'* ."

Not being a Royal *(a fondness of **Kir Royale** doesn't count) the year* 2004 ano domini had, for me, simply been a *'sod of a year.'* medically speaking.

It had started in late 2003 with a date with a certain orthopaedic Surgeon who appeared to be called *Mufi* by all the nurses, and who, from my very first consultation insisted that I called him likewise. I suspect it may have been because he thought I might have trouble with Doctor Mufifikuma, not, I hasten to add his correct name, but I think you will take the point I am making.

I have to say *Mufi* was a charming man and rates in the 'top one' of *all* the Surgeons who operated on my right foot on December 22nd 2003.

For the previous 3 years or so, I had suffered, bravely of course, with an arthritic right foot (hereinafter referred to, as our legal friends would say, as an A.R.F., of the first part - which would, of course, technically speaking be incorrect being that the foot, far from being of the first part, is quite clearly of the last part, being substantially attached, as it was at that time, to the end of the right leg).

If you take away the small matter of not being able to walk properly, a number of good things can come out of an A.R.F.

1. *An A.R.F. gives you* a Doctor's note which, enables you to use a Golf Buggy in the club's monthly medals, even when it's not raining.

2. *It gives you,* when travelling by air, the privilege of 'Wheel Chair Assist' meaning you are whisked through check-in ignoring the queue, given a ride on a personal transporter to the boarding Gate, and escorted first on the plane, with the advantage of stowing your luggage before the crowd's rampage up the aisle.

3. *It gives you* a seat at the front of the plane *(for complete safety it should of course be at the back, after all, who ever heard of a plane reversing into a mountain).*

4. *It gives you* extra leg room - perfect if you have an extra leg.

AND

5. *It gives you* the devoted and personal service of a dedicated and especially attentive cabin steward....normally called Jason, or Rodney.

My A.R.F. also gave me 5 weeks of being pushed everywhere around our Tenerife winter home and environs, in a wheel-chair, by my long suffering, and increasingly muscular wife Polly (of whom more later).

This period was forced to a premature conclusion, when, one day whilst Polly was playing golf; I decided that my own biceps could do with a little hardening if I was ever to win another in-house arm wrestling contest.

I set out to test my own muscle power. Close to the pool there are three steps, alongside which is a fairly steep, but quite obviously negotiable Wheel-chair slope. I surveyed the slope and decided that my biceps were up to the job. *That* truth was never revealed, because half way up the slope, I discovered that the further the front wheels went UP, the more my centre of gravity projected DOWN. With a cry of humiliation I watched the front wheels come off the ground, and, in slow motion my legs, and then my feet flipped over my head as I executed a near perfect backward somersault. Score 10 for complexity, 0 for the style.

I lay in a heap, my knees in my mouth and the wheel chair on my neck. The wheels were spinning and so was my head. Everyone around was still and quiet, but I knew they were silently laughing their socks off.   Isabel, the resident *'socrosista'* came to my aid, at about the same time that I came to the conclusion that I needed a chair with a low centre of gravity and a powerful engine.

Within days I had swallowed my hurting pride, thanked Isabel, and hired a smart little motorised three-wheeler from the local motorised three-wheeler hire shop.   I called it Eric.   Eric and I hit it off from the word go.   Together we could attain speeds of up to 4 miles an hour, and I was able to terrify those pool-side lounger's who had witnessed my humiliation, and many who hadn't. They would lie there, decadently, even mockingly, tanning their fully functioning feet beneath the swaying palm trees on our home complex, taunting me with their wiggling *'dedos del pie'*   - literally translated meaning *'fingers of the feet'* or Spanish for toes, we are in Spain after all - as I passed by.

Eric and I enjoyed each others company for sixty glorious days, and there was a lump in my throat and a dent in my wallet when, following a Management decision, I returned Eric to the motorised three-wheeler hire shop.   He was replaced by a silver topped walking stick. A name for which never seemed appropriate.

In order to enjoy the before mentioned events, there had, of course, been certain disadvantages. First I had to go through an orthopaedic Surgical procedure known, in lay terms, as a fuse-and-screw job.   Because, as my consultant surgeon, and now great friend *Mufi* had explained, there was nothing wrong with my foot that £3,500 plus V.A.T. wouldn't cure.

I will not bore you with the details .... but here are the details.

Just in time for Christmas 2003, *Mufi* took my ankle joint apart, grafted some new bone into the joint *(courtesy, he said, of an uneaten chicken drumstick he found in the nurse's fridge)*, and then fused the whole lot together again, pinning the resulting 'rigid' joint with two evil looking staples.   This made it the most unpleasant joint I'd had since the early sixties.

I spent Christmas plastered in plaster. And the winter alternating between the afore-mentioned wheel-chair assist at Gatwick or Tenerife Sud airports, or wheel-chair assist, between my home in Tenerife and the bodega on the corner.

Three visits back to England resulted in the discovery that the evil looking staples driven through the ankle bone were no longer driven through the ankle bone and were now free and floating just below the surface of the skin, giving the promise of a little remedial surgery to look forward to in the coming summer of 2004.

And so, I 'enjoyed' a hot sunny winter spent with my leg in plaster itching like a tomcats tummy. Baths taken with one leg inelegantly draped over the side of the bath, and the ignominy of always being last into the bar.

Ankle saga nearly over.   I arrived back in England in May.   *Mufi* decided it would be best to get the further *'small'* operation *'out of the way'* without delay.

"You will have to be an 'overnighter' " he said, "but I will simply *'open the wound"* and we will have the *'staples'* in a pot and away before you know it, unless" he added, "you would like to keep them as a souvenir".

Polly answered for me then, in much the same way as she had 15 years previously, when, having chopped off the index finger of my right hand at the first knuckle and left it underneath the lawn mower, the hospital had asked the same question.....they had received much the same answer. "I'll get rid of them then shall I" said *Mufi*. Further dialogue was unnecessary, All agreed, job done and dusted by late May.   From then on me and my walking stick looked forward to a summer of Golf with no pain and a following winter like the winters of my youth.

But fate is a fickle friend, and had no plans to be my number one buddy in the year 2004

CHAPTER 3
THE LOVELY NITA

JUNE 2004

The operation was over. I had abandoned my crutches and now walked, elegantly some would say, with the aid of a smart silver topped cane (sterling silver of course) that my wife had bought me for our silver wedding in 1989.   At the time it was intended as a stage prop for when I did my impersonation of Frankie Vaughan, singing

'Give me the moonlight,
Give me the girl,
And leave the rest, (throaty chuckle and high kick
revealing split trousers)
To me....heeee.

Then, I had looked like a cherubic, though ageing Frankie Vaughan, now I looked for all the world like a partially arthritic Hercule Poirot. Mufi had continued my old prescription for an anti-

inflammatory alelgesic called Dicofenac...and so....
after I had run out (or perhaps in my case....limped
out) of my last handful, I went to see my *new* local
GP in order to get a repeat prescription.

Let me tell you about the GP who was to
become my second love. Her name was Dr.
Hakelin. She was young, about my daughter's
age, (mid thirties), bouncy and beautiful with a
smile as big as the room. Her first name was
Nita, and although I could not know it then, as
the summer progressed, life saving Nita was to
become identified in my mind, and subsequently
the minds of my family, as *'The lovely Nita'*
        "Good Morning," looking down at her notes
"Basil" she said, looking up at me and showing me
that smile for the first time.
        "Hello Doctor. How am I?" I said, trying to
establish in her mind that I was not about to
become a miserable and twice weekly pain in
the prescription pad, but an *'occasional'* patient
with whom she could enjoy some light hearted
banter. She smiled. "That's for you to tell me"
she said.
        "I'm fine" I said, "I've only called in to get a
repeat prescription for my Dicofenac." She tapped
her pen on her desk.
        "I don't want to give you any more" she said.
        "You haven't given me any yet" I answered
with a grin you could hear at the other end of the
car park.

"No, but according to your notes you were taking them for the whole of last winter."

"They were for my A.R.F." I said,

"your A.R.F?" she said

"My Arthritic Right Foot" I explained, realising she probably didn't have the same legal friends that I did.

"Do they work well?" she said.

I thought about that, "I don't really know what the pain would be like without them" I answered

"I want you to try" she said "Lets say for one month."

"Why?" I asked, interested, not annoyed

"They are not good for your tummy" she said, "much better if you can get by without."

"OK," I said, "I'll come back, crippled in pain, in a month." I smiled to show it was a joke. She smiled back, to show she understood.

"Before you go" she said "you're nearly 62 years old."

"I know" I said

"You don't appear to have had a cholesterol test since.......ever."

"I think I did once" I said, "I remember having a plate of macaroni cheese before I went." She smiled tiredly, obviously heard that one before.

"I'd like you to arrange a blood test with the nurse."

"OK" I said

"Now" she said, "Today."

"On my way out." I said

"Whilst we're about it" she said "I like to look at your PSA."

"I've left it on the kitchen table" I said, another tired, I've heard it all before smile.

"It is important" she said, "At your age things can start to go wrong."

'The lovely Nita' got that right and no mistake. For although neither of us knew it then, whilst her prescription pad was to remain safe, I was to become a definite pain in two other areas of her anatomy.

It was June 8th 2004

CHAPTER 4
THE BLOOD(Y) TEST

JUNE 2004

When I left the surgery on that June morning, my only pre-occupation was whether the lack of my tablets would mean that my ARF was going to effect the golfing summer that I was looking forward to.

I was half-hearted about the blood tests. Oh, I made the appointment, the first, for just three days after I had seen *'The lovely Nita.'*

"Remember" said the nurse. "Nothing to eat or drink for 10 hours before the blood test."

"I won't forget" I said. After all, the blood test was at 9.30 in the morning, and I would be sleeping for most of the 10 hours before that. I forgot. I woke at 8.00, jumped out of bed, and went to the kitchen and made myself a 'wake-up' cup of coffee.

"Good morning" said the nurse getting out her syringe and tourniquet.

"when did you last eat or drink?"

"I had a cup of coffee whe...............oh dear." For Bright Basil the penny had dropped even before the sentence was finished. The nurse tut-tutted and then arranged a second test for a week's time, at the later hour of 10.45. "Don't forget, she said, don't eat, don't drink and don't even think about it from midnight on the night before."

"Understood" I said with a hang-dog smile, "I really won't forget."

The trouble with first thing in the morning is, not only has your body only just woken up, but your brain is struggling to do the same thing. I remembered *not* to have a cup of coffee. Instead, having staggered out of bed at the crack of ten o'clock, I crab-crawled to the fridge, opened the door, and groped for the carton of orange juice I knew Polly would have left in the door tray. I poured myself a refreshing glass in a champagne flute and leaned against the fridge enjoying the experience of a bucks fizz which lacked only the champagne to make it perfect. "What are you doing?" said Polly as she walked into the kitchen having been up for about half a day. She looked meaningfully at the half empty glass. That's all it needed, because, when all is said and done Bright Basil is pretty quick on the up-take.

"Ouch" I said. "Have I blown it again?"

"Yes" said Polly, "probably on purpose." I raised my hands in mock surrender.

"Unintentional" I said, "Honest." Polly chose not to answer. I quietly poured the remaining quarter glass down the sink, very thankful that it was *'sin champagne'* and slithered out to my car. I went to the clinic and confessed to the nurse.

"Can't be done" she said, "I'll make you another appointment for 8.30 tomorrow morning. That should make it easier, just remember eat and drink nothing after 10 o'clock tonight." This time she didn't labour the point. "and make sure you're back here by 8.30, I have a busy day." I, did, I didn't, I did and by 8.35 a.m. the blood was out of my arm and in a little plastic tube with my name on it.

The next day, Polly and I drove to Wales. From Holyhead we caught a ferry to Dublin, from Dublin we drove to Buncrana in County Donegal. No way the nurse would find me now. We were in County Donegal for our annual rain-worshipping ceremony on the golf courses of Ballyliffin, North West, and Green Castle, three of the best golf course we have ever played, lush and green beyond believe, probably on account of the fact that in has rained non - stop in County Donegal for the last 14 years.

This is not a golf travel book, and so I propose to tell you NOTHING of the weeks golf in Donegal. I was brilliant of course, but it is for others to explain the degree of my brilliance and why I never won a single prize. What I do want to tell you about is our subsequent week-end in Dublin.

We stayed in a fine hotel in the Blackrock area, a Hotel that this IBS (?) *(International Best Seller - DREAM ON BASIL)* does not need to name or promote. We met two lots of very close Tenerife winter friends for lunch at their own golf club, the lovely Mill Town in Dublin. This same IBS makes no apology for naming Norman and Ursula Butler and Mary and John Rafferty. The friendship and hospitality they show us in Tenerife (which is considerable) was, eclipsed, if such a thing was possible, by the hospitality shown on their home turf. The lunch was delightful. It is a typical 'old world' golf club, and I was particularly impressed by the way the Maitre D' came to the table and asked "Would you like an aperitif Professor?" to Norman, "and you Doctor?" to John, whilst complete ignoring the fact that I am a member of the AA. I didn't make a scene, but enjoyed a delightful lunch.

Have I mentioned my A.R.F. Well, you will remember that I have ground clearance for the use of a buggy. Unfortunately, Mill Town is much too posh for buggies other than those that are privately owned. Norman, pulled a few strings and persuaded a friend of his to loan me his own personal buggy, Now to say it was **State of the Art** would be to exaggerate. To say it was **In a State** would not. It was a three wheeler that would make Eric ashamed to be considered of the same species, although, it must be said, it had a turn of speed that would have made Harley wish he'd have married a Davidson. For seventeen holes things went tolerably well. It was raining, (par for the course) I had scored around 85 (around 20 over par for the course) but I was still on the buggy............but not for long. On the 18th I hit an appallingly bad drive, although on reflection, it probably wasn't that good. However, I recovered with a stunning 5 iron which put me back within sight of the golf course, a following 8 iron put me within just a mile or two of the Green, or as Norman exclaimed - "Well Basil, you appear to be back on the planet." It was only then that things began to go wrong. In my exuberance, I accelerated up the 18th fairway. The front half of the buggy (the half to which my hands were attached) responded, cat like, to my touch. The rear half of the buggy (the half to which my backside was attached) had clearly had enough, and refused to join the fronts half's mad dash to the eighteenth green and home.. I had a choice. Should I keep hold of the front half and allow myself to be dragged along on my front side, or should I let go with my arms and allow myself to be deposited on my backside. I chose to be indecisive, and watched, together with my partners, as the front half described a dying circle to the front at the same time as the back half described a dead lump at the back. I did not choose to be, but was in the middle. I held on, for a while. The result was that I was dragged along on my backside for a number of yards before finally accepting that I was achieving less than a missionary in a brothel. I let go. The 18th fairway of Mill Town now had THREE dead lumps. The front end, the back end.... and me.　　It took nearly half an hour to get us all re-assembled both into a cohesive unit and into a story to be dined off for months to come.　　We do what we can to brighten the ordinary life.

On the morning of June 24th The Surgery telephoned.

"Mr Jay" said the receptionist "it's the surgery here."

"Good morning" I said, I don't think I'd ever been telephoned, on business, by a Doctor before, it's usually for a game of golf or to appear as an expert witness in an up coming murder game or pub quiz.

"Dr. Hakelin would like you to come and see her....today.....is 5 o'clock alright?"

"Five o'clock will be fine" I said, almost speechless.

"Who was that?" said Polly.

"The surgery", I said, "The Doctor wants me to go and see her at 5 o'clock."

"She probably just has your blood test results." Polly said.

Although I was not worried, after all, if your cholesterol is up, you just eat less cheese. Nevertheless, it was a fairly long day.

"Hello Basil" that smile, "Sit down."

"Thank you" I said, "I've never been summoned before, except by the police, and they don't really count."

"I have your blood test results."

"Yesss"

"Your cholesterol is very high at 8.9."

"OK, no more cheese, no more eggs."

"Yes that will help," pause, "but" she steepled her fingers "but I want to come back to that, a little later, we have found something a little more worrying." I began to screw my toes up in my shoes....like you do.

"Your PSA is 12...It should be between 0.1 and 0.4 maximum."

"0.1 and 0.4 eh" I said knowingly. "What does it all mean?" I asked

"It indicates a problem with your Prostate, and at that level it could mean cancer," Hurrah for the new trend of telling it like it is. I thought.

"I would like you to come back to the surgery tomorrow morning and Dr. Traynor will carry out a DRE."

"Oh," I said, not completely taking it in "Why Dr Traynor and not you?"

"I thought you might prefer to have a man stick his finger up your bum."

I raised my eyebrows; she gave me her brightest smile.

"A DRE" she said, resting her chin on her clenched fists, "Is a Digital Rectal Examination - shall we say 9 o'clock."

"9 o'clock" I said, avoiding a discussion on my preferences.

She talked to me for some minutes more; she told me how the PSA can be raised for other reasons as well as cancer.   Infection, enlargement etc.

She told me how I did not appear to have any of the symptoms.   Couldn't go, couldn't stop going, needing to get up several times in the night etc.

All the sort of 'Old Men' things, that we *'nearly'* 62 year old youngsters have only heard about.   She explained how it always pays to be careful, to take precautions, she reminded me that this was why she wanted to look at my PSA - a joke did not seem appropriate this time.   She smiled me out of the door saying "Don't worry; I am sure it will be fine."

I walked out of the surgery, through our beautiful village square, and home to the pretty cottage where we intend to live out our days.

"Well?" said Polly

"I want us to go out for a really good meal tonight," I said.   We went to Le Soufflé, one of our favourite restaurants which overlooks the village green.   We discussed the whole thing over monk-fish tails wrapped in Parma ham, a bottle of Champagne and a half bottle of Chablis.

Well, one cannot let standards slip.   Then we went home and went to bed.

But the Tigers came that night

There were three of them.   It was very late when they came, I would guess about 4 o'clock. The darkest of the night had gone, but the dawn, and the dicky birds, was still far away.

The first of my Tigers was 'Fear',

He was small, but he gave the promise of terror to come.   He nuzzled around my mind. I could hear him "It may be cancer you know; 'the lovely Nita' did **telephone** you and ask you to go in.   That must be a bit unusual - surely if it was routine they would have just sent a note. **and,** she has asked you to go and see this Dr. Traynor **first thing** in the morning. It doesn't sound too good to me. No, I reckon its cancer for sure, **and falling off that bloody buggy probably didn't help.**"

My second Tiger was 'Regret',

"Why,?" it whispered, "Why did you waste ten days by not listening to the Nurse?   10 days wasted, and all for a cup of coffee and a glass of orange juice. It was irresponsible to, ruin not only ONE blood test, but TWO." I didn't answer; after all, it was only a Tiger in my head.

"If you DO have cancer, that ten days could be important.   You're a fool, and its no good saying that you thought the test was only for cholesterol, 'The lovely Nita' did tell you that she wanted to look at your PSA.   Your trouble is that you are always too busy trying to make a joke about things Instead, you should have been asking her what she was really worried about."

My third Tiger was '*Hope*'

And his voice was the loudest of all

"Of course it's not cancer.   Think about it, there are dozens of symptoms to prostate cancer, and the 'Lovely Nita' told you that you haven't had any of them."   Hope ticked them off for me

"1. Needing to go to the loo all the time.

2. Wanting to go but not being able to,

3. Stopping and starting whilst you stand in a line staring at the wall.

4. Passing blood.

5. Passing the time of day.

6. Passing the salt.

7. Passing out."

It was getting silly now, but, as 'Hope' pointed out, not nearly as silly as

'*Fear*' and '**Regret**'.

"No" finished off '**Hope**', "for sure, you've just got a bit of an infection, the worst thing you're going to have to face is Dr Traynor's finger up your backside."

There you go then.   QED.   There's nothing wrong with MY prostate

Before my Tigers started to argue amongst themselves, I drifted off into a dreamless slumber, and my last waking thoughts were

"I wonder why the lovely Nita thought I'd prefer Dr Traynor's finger?"

CHAPTER 5
A DITIGAL EXPERIENCE

JUNE 2004

I was early at the surgery the next morning. My Tigers had been chased away by the sunshine.

On my previous visits, previous RARE visits to the doctors, I had aimlessly thumbed through HOUSE BEAUTIFUL, COUNTRY LIFE, or, if the Doctor was an enthusiast, WHAT CAR? Oh what a squandered youth, what a waste of educational opportunity. This morning, I allowed myself to glance, albeit furtively, at the wealth of pamphlets colourfully arranged on the table by the door. Such evocative titles. Who could fail to be moved by *'Talking About Bowels'*. Whose knees would not squeeze together with delight at the prospect of thumbing through *'Your Bladder and You'*, or eyes mist over when contemplating *'Smoking will it kill you?'* Who would not dribble in anticipation of that great read *'Your Prostate, things you should know'* Surreptitiously, with the slim pamphlet on my knee so the subject could not be obvious to a nosy neighbour, I devoured the information contained within those colourful pages.

DID YOU KNOW? - *The prostate is the size of a walnut* (at least it should be - at that moment I feared mine might be more like a coconut).

DID YOU KNOW? - *The prostate doesn't have a lot to do.*   Working well, it produces semen, an important role at 32, less important at *'nearly'* 62.

Working inefficiently it makes you want to go to the loo ten times a night, it turns a stream into a dribble, and a cosy evening in a restaurant into a stumbled obstacle race for the nearest Gents.   It is very prone to cancer.   By sticking your finger (or preferably someone else's) up your back passage you can feel it, and stroke it, and discern whether it is the size of a walnut whilst being a smooth as pecan, or if it is lumpy like an overweight prune. If it is enlarged it presses against the bladder, it is then that you have the constant urge to chase your golf ball into the bushes, and then linger for a while.

I was beginning to get a 'feel' if you will forgive the pun, for this DRE.   I was now confident that I could ask Dr Traynor the right questions.

There was a ping *'Basil Jay to Room 2'* said the flashing lights.   I rushed out of the waiting room before the lights had time to add, *'Dr. Traynor has his gloves on and is waiting'*.

"Come In" he said.   I came in

"Do sit down" he said. I did sit down

"Good Morning" he smiled,

"Good Morning Doctor," I smiled back.

"Doctor Hakelin has asked me to see you."

"Yes"

"Did she explain why?"

"Yes Doctor she did."

"Would you like me to explain exactly what I am looking for and why?"

"I rather think I would Doctor, thank you."

"Your PSA, That stands for Prostate Specific Antigen. This should measure on a scale between 0.1 and 0.4. PSA leaks into the blood stream, and from this we can measure the level."

"I see" I said; I didn't

"A higher PSA suggests a problem; the problem could be cancer, although it equally could be something rather more benign." He smiled. "But it is important that we check it out."

"I see" I said. I did.

"What I am going to do is ask you some questions that will help form a profile. This will also help us in monitoring any future treatment by regular up-dates."

"I see" I said; I thought I did.

"After the questions, the answers to which I will enter on the computer, I will examine your prostate by inserting my…….."

"I think I understand that bit Doctor - I also think I know what you will be looking for"…He raised an eyebrow……"I've just read it in your Pamphlet," I explained.

"That's good" he said "Shall we begin then?" The questions were easy, neither of us had to wear gloves. When they were over he stood up.

"Just take of your trousers and lie on the couch. You can keep your socks on."

"Just like sex" I thought irrationally. I heard the squeak of latex and the cracking of fingers. "Just like sex" I thought again.

"Just lie on your side" he said, "And face the wall" I did as I was asked

"Now this may be a little uncomfortable, but it won't last long." It was, and it didn't

"OK," he said, handing me a tissue, you can get dressed again.

In a post digital glow, we sat next to each other...a cigarette would have been nice. I tried to imagine Dr Traynor with two cigarettes in his mouth behind a flickering lighter. The image wouldn't quite come.

"Well" he said, "I am not an expert, but I can feel something"

"Oh dear" I said.

"It doesn't feel lumpy"

"That's good" I said, "Isn't it?" I added. He smiled, sadly I thought.

"But it does feel enlarged."

"Oh dear" I said again.

"I am going to refer you to the Oncology." That was a new word, "To the Oncology consultant, his name is Mr Breading. He's a nice man."

"And an expert" I thought

"He should see you within a few days"

"So soon?" I asked in wonderment

"It's the new NHS Code" he said

"Thank you" I said "very much, your explanations have been very clear and very gratefully received."

"Is there anything else?" he said throwing the rubber glove into the bin.

"No" I said "Thank you" I added

"Try not to worry too much" he said.

"I'll try," I said.

I left the room, but I didn't tell him about the Tigers.

TIGER TIGER BURNING BRIGHT

The Tigers barely crept in to my night.

Fear, tried hard to disturb me.

"That Dr Traynor, is obviously very worried, why else would he send you to a consultant. AND within a few days.   That doesn't sound very NHS, to me, unless, of course, he thinks everything is very advanced and he has to act quickly."

Hope was close by

"Rubbish" she said, "He explained he wasn't an expert, he said it didn't feel lumpy.   I think he just wants to be sure, that's why he's sending you to a specialist.   What good news that you will be seen within a few days, once the specialist has seen you you will be able to get on with you summer and your golf".

I lay there for a long time thinking about our summer.   A couple of weeks and we were heading back to Tenerife for a few days sunshine. Polly had organised something special for my Birthday at the end of July. Then we were then off to Deauville for a long week-end at the wonderful Hotel du Golf, treating Tania and Nigel and our beautiful little Grandson Jack.

Then there was a trip to Paris, a short business trip to Gibraltar, and the whole family coming to us for a long week-end dinner. As soon as Mr Breading had confirmed there was nothing wrong we could get on with our lives.

CHAPTER 6
A WHITE PLASTIC CUP

JULY 2004

Just two days later an envelope, later to become oh so familiar, would have arrived on the door mat if we had had one.   As it was it arrived through the letter box and on to a small area of Wilton Tufted that covered the outer hall.   *NHS TRUST* it said.   I took it into the kitchen.

"That's quick" I said

"That's good" said Polly.   I opened it

An appointment has been made for **MR BASIL JAY** *to see* **MR BREADING** *on* **TUESDAY 3RD JULY 2004** *at* **2.15.P.M.** *Please report to the* **ONCOLOGY DEPARTMENT** *on arrival and bring a* **URINE SAMPLE** *with you.*

If you are unable to keep this appointment it is important that you contact **APPOINTMENTS** *without delay*

"That's good" I said again - "just 10 days"

"That's also the day we fly to Tenerife" said Polly thumbing through the diary which is so important to our lives, and, which I am sure she had surgically grafted onto her finger-tips soon after we were married.

"Oh dear" I said, "I'll see if I can change the appointment"

"No you won't" said Poll, "If anything we change the flight...but.....I don't think that will be necessary"

"Why?" I said, fully realising it must mean that the flight left after the appointment.

"Your appointment is at 2.15 and we don't fly till 6.0. We don't have to be at Gatwick until 4.30. It takes 45 minutes.... traffic permitting, which means, as long as we are away by 3.45 we will be fine" I didn't bother to check the arithmetic.

"An hour and a half should be plenty of time for an experienced Oncologist," I said, not having the remotest idea whether it was plenty of time for an experienced Oncologist or not, but generally believing that anyone who was an 'ologist' of any description had not become one by being slow out of the starting blocks.

We arrived at the Hospital in good time and found the Oncology department in minutes flat.   I was clutching tightly to a miniature shampoo bottle - of the sort stolen from hotel bedrooms - and into which, I had, before we left home, dribbled, with difficulty, an inch or two of champagne enhanced wee. I reflected, that a week ago I hadn't even heard of Oncology, and now, I spoke it like a native. The receptionist ticked me off (her list) and said sweetly "Just take a seat Mr Jay, the nurse will see you in a moment" I took a seat, and the nurse ignored me for a lifetime - at least it seemed like it.

I picked up a magazine and looked around me. The waiting room was heaving. There was a man with a badge leaning against a trolley and dispensing weak tea and even weaker coffee in white plastic cups. He smiled as he caught my eye and silently gestured to a cup. I smiled back and equally silently shook my head. There was a man with a white beard and a cheery smile. I was to bump into the man (though not always the smile) several times during my coming summer of self-discovery, as together we trod the prostate path.

"Mr Jay, my dear, will you just fill............?" I held up my Holiday Inn miniature shampoo bottle about to say knowingly,

"No need my dear, here's one I filled up earlier,

"This form" she finished. I cleverly concealed the small bottle in the palm of my hand.

"Of course" I said, and then regaining the initiative "Do you have a pen?"

She gave me one. I looked at the form, the questions were identical to those posed by Dr Traynor's computer. I racked my brains to ensure that the answers I gave were the same.

"Mr Jay" I looked up, it was the nurse.   I held out the form, she ignored it and offered my instead a white plastic cup.

"Coffee" I thought, "how kind"

"Just pop along to the toilet and give me a sample" she said in a voice which only the roar of traffic on the M25 would have prevented the residents of Reigate and Redhill hearing.

"I've brought............." I began, revealing the previously palmed bottle.

"We'll have a sterile one I think" she smiled, "the loo's just around the Corner".   I took the cup and standing up made my way through the rows of patients.

"I'll collect it in a minute" she called.   Nobody laughed, their dignity had already been stolen.

I was back in my chair.   I had my white plastic cup in one hand and was trying to thumb through an old copy of 'Hello' with the other.

"Put the cup on the floor" said Polly.   I might kick it over I thought

"Don't kick it over" said Polly "Push it under the chair". I did, amongst several others holding remnants of long discarded cold tea or coffee that

had been dispensed by the man with the badge........or had he, and was it.

I still had my form.

"Mr Jay, can I have.................?" I panicked and reached for the cup and held it out to her.

"My pen" she smiled.   I guiltily fished in my pocket and found the plastic Bic with the chewed end.

"Thank you" she said "and I'll take the........" I held out the cup

"form now" she smiled again and confided "you can bring that" nodding at the cup "in with you when you come."   Such joy my cup runneth over. Not literally of course, although I could swear that a tiny crack was causing the smallest of seepages to leave small damp spots on my beige trousers.

Some time passed.

"Mr Jay" I recognised the voice but was no longer excited.   "Come with me if you wouldn't mind." I followed, she took me to a small cubicle and opened a curtain.

"Just take of your trousers" I'd been here before

"Can I keep my socks on?" I said.   She didn't smile

"Just slip that gown on and come into room 8" she indicated a door with a Number 8 painted on it.   My trousers were still around one ankle, even though my arms were through the front loading sleeves of a gown that would have fitted me a treat when I was about twelve, when the curtains were pulled aside and nurse's head appeared.

"Mr Breading is ready for you" she said.   I hung my trousers up on the floor and followed her through the door marked 8.   Inside was a burly rugby player with hands like hams.

"Good Afternoon Mr Jay" he said in a loud and cheerful voice.   "I'm Tony Breading"

"Hello" I said.

"Dr. Traynor has asked me to have a look at you. You know why I Suppose?". I nodded, as I rather supposed I did.

"You're familiar with a DRE?" he said questioningly. Was *familiar* the word, I looked at his rugger ball holding hands and mentally compared them with the more piano playing fingers of Dr. Traynor.

"I rather think I am" I said.

"Well" he said Dr Traynor would like me to just check you out and then we can go on from there. Just pop up on the couch, lie on your side and face the wall" Why I thought do you always have to face the wall, "and I'll just have a bit of a look around." I popped on the couch, lay on my side and faced the wall. Then he had a bit of a look around.

"OK" he said, handing me a tissue. "All over, you can climb down now" I climbed down and pulling my gown about me sat back on the chair in front if his desk. I missed the post digital glow, and barely thought of cigarettes.

"There's definitely something there" he said, so I am going to send you for a TRUS"

"A Truss" I said confusion obviously showing on my face

"One S" he said, I was obviously not the first to be confused.

"Only one?" I asked, feeling an acronym coming on

"Transrectal Ultrasound" he said

"Oh, a Transrectal Ultrasound" I said - casting around for even ONE S

"It's an Ultrasound scan and a biopsy. Nothing to worry about, we'll do it within two weeks, and the Doctor will explain exactly what he is going to do. So, just go and sit outside and the nurse will come and make an appointment for the TRUS and also an appointment to see me again for the results clinic. We'll soon sort you out as soon as we know what we're dealing with." He stopped as if working out whether or not now was a good time to take a breath. Miraculously the nurse had re-appeared. She led me out, sat me down, and then ignored me for the next twenty minutes.

Eventually I went to her and explained that we were going on holiday and if we were going to catch our plane we needed to be going now. She had obviously forgotten me and was, for once apologetic and almost human.

"I'm so sorry Mr Jay, let's look at the calendar". Within minutes I had a date for my TRUS. I was going to have a Transrectal for my birthday - on the 28th July. I would be 62 years, 2 DRE's and a Transrectal old.

Nursie also made me an appointment for the results clinic on the 17th August. My cup really did runneth over.

I thanked her, gathered up my Tigers, and Polly and I set of for Gatwick, Tenerife and 10 days away from it all. With me I took, what will become as enduring a piece of advice as 'yellow snow' NEVER DRINK FROM A WHITE PLASTIC CUP

A TIGERS JUST A BIG PUSSY CAT WITH STRIPES

Tenerife was very restful.   The sun shone and prostates, dignity stripping nurses and latex gloves seemed a million miles away. The Tigers were pretty well behaved.   It has to be said that they still prowled around at the periphery of my mind.

*Every now and again **'Fear'**   would raise himself up and roar into my ear.*
*"Don't forget you have **CANCER** you know, the big 'C' "*

*'**Hope,**' however was never far away to whisper - "It will be alright, just you see, remember you have had none of those symptoms that the international best seller '**Prostate Cancer - all you need to know**' spoke about."*

*It was about this time that a new Tiger joined my little group. I called him '**Resignation'**, and as the weeks progressed, in a strange way, he became the most comforting of them all.   But in Tenerife he had very little to say.   "Just lay back and enjoy the sun" was his only contribution, "There is nothing you can do now but wait".*
*And so for 10 days I lay back, enjoyed the sun, and waited   and in that Time '**Regret**' visited me not once.*

CHAPTER 7
THE LETTERS

JULY 2004

I was furious. No I was not, I was incandescent. Everything had appeared to be so much in control. My biopsy was to be on July 28th (My sixty second birthday) The result was to be given to me just 3 weeks later on August 17th. A long time to wait to have it confirmed whether you have cancer or not, but I had prepared for it, and the mind has an interesting way of accepting *'facts of life'*, and one of my *'facts of life'* was that I was going to have a biopsy on my birthday, and be told the result 17 days later. Ces't la Vie, or as the French say.... *Such is life*

So, here I was, first day back from my days in the sun with my short-term future clearly mapped out in my mind.

The envelope lay on the doormat (alright, we've been through that - in the absence of a doormat, it lay on the floor).   Thanks to my new big Tiger friend, *'Resignation,' the others, particularly 'Fear' and 'Regret'* had become like little kittens playfully cavorting on the edges of my mind.

'Hope' was ever present, vying with *'Resignation'* for attention.

Against this background, I tore open the envelope and read.

Dear **MR JAY**

Due to unforeseen circumstances, it is necessary to change your appointment with **MR BREADING** *presently arranged for the* **17**th **AUGUST 2004**

An alternative appointment has been arranged for you to attend the **ONCOLOGY** *DEPARTMENT on the* **30**th **SEPTEMBER 2004**

What !!!

To be attended by **MR BREADING** *or one of his team.*

I was angry...I was more than angry, I was furious, I was more than furious, I was suicidal.   I had a spleen to vent, and by God I vented it.

In my mind I wrote.............

I   HAVE   YOUR   LETTER...................
UNBLOODYFORGIVEABLE..............TOTALLY
UNACCEPTABLE..........HOW   DARE   YOU
PEOPLE................PLAYING   GOD   WITH
PEOPLES.......................I   WILL   ACCEPT
NOTHING   LESS   THAN..............A   LETTER   TO

MY M.P....................................I BLAME THE GOVERNMENT.......................HAVE YOU NOTHING BETTER TO DO.........BE SURE TO HAVE THE COURTESY TO.................WHO DO YOU THINK YOU ARE DEALING WITH......IF I HAVE NOT HEARD WITHIN..................

On paper I wrote.

Dear Sirs,

I was very disappointed to receive your letter. I do appreciate that you are labouring under considerable difficulties, but find the delay in my attending results clinic quite unacceptable.

(I liked the 'quite' it suggests a well measured response from someone who is considering all sides of the problem and not simply ranting on their own behalf)

To date I have been very pleased with the speed with which everything has been dealt with. My GP arranged a DRE within 24 hours and an appointment for a specialist DRE 10 days after that.

(A month ago I didn't even know what a DRE was; NOW I had had TWO within the space of TWO Sundays)

I was very pleased to have had my TRUS biopsy arranged within 3 weeks

(I refrained from reminding them that there own pamphlet states 'we will arrange your TRUS within 14 days)

I was also very pleased to have an appointment made for the results clinic just 3 weeks after the biopsy.

(A reminder that their _second_ pamphlet said 'we aim to arrange your results clinic within 14 days of your biopsy - also seemed a little churlish)

*However, I know you will understand that, even on that time-scale it will have been almost 8 weeks from my first DRE to having the severity of the **cancer** confirmed. I had 'steeled 'myself for this, but your new time appointment schedule adds a further 8 weeks to the waiting time. Quite apart from the mental strain of such a long wait, I worry very much whether such a delay could seriously affect my treatment options.*

(Now for the big finish)

I leave myself confidently in your hands, but would sincerely request that you try to find me an earlier appointment time.
I look forward to your favourable response.
Kindest regards.

I calmly signed the letter, folded it and slipped it into a top of the range cream laid envelope - (no point in appearing a cheapskate).   I then called down the stairs to my wife.

"POLLY, I'M GOING BLOODY PRIVATE".

THE TIGERS CAME RATHER EARLIER THAT NIGHT
'Fear' bounded into my mind
claws unsheathed, fangs bared, eyes gleaming with evil excitement.

"They don't care about you" he roared, "You are just a number, and pretty low on their list to boot.   Just think about it, Lung Cancer by the armful, Heart disease by the cartload, Breast Cancers by the bucketful, and add to that, Dementia, Parkinson's, Leukaemia, Hodgekinsons, MS, ME, M Bloody T.   And you, a minor case of Prostate, Bloody Cancer.

They will put you at the bottom of the list, mark my words, this is the first of a million cancelled appointments, and then, one day, I am so sorry Mr Jay, But in the 29 months since we first saw you the cancers spread to your left ear and your big toe.   There's nothing we can do for you now. But, the good news is we have the address of a very good Hospice who will ease you through the gate so beautifully you'll wish you'd have gone years ago."

"Rubbish" said 'Hope,'
"They've caught it early, you'll be fine"

"You would have been fine" roared 'Fear'

"if it hadn't been for all the priorities before you. Holidays in the Caribbean, Ski-ing Trips to Austria, a fact finding visit to Outer Mongolia. Compassionate leave because Auntie Gladys has had a baby.

Maternity leave, Paternity leave, Fraternity leave, Don't want to come to work today' leave. And all the time, you're appointments are cancelled, and your cancer is growing and growing and growing and growing. It's in your bones, your lungs, your stomach, your bowels, ...you're dead"

'Hope' purred,

and, looking like a big soft pussycat nuzzled up and whispered "Ignore him, these are all kind dedicated people, you are as important to them as any one else. You'll see, if the biopsy shows anything serious - and it won't - they will bring your appointment forward without a doubt. You will be fine" I believed, and slipped into a dreamless sleep.

Two mornings later there was a new envelope on the doormat

Dear **MR JAY**

Please note that your appointment to see **MR BREADING** *arranged for the* **30th SEPTEMBER 2004** *has been changed*

An alternative appointment has been arranged for you to attend the **ONCOLOGY** *on The* **31st AUGUST 2004**

"That's better" I said to Polly, "But I'll still go private."

"Why don't you have a word with Dr. Hakelin first?" she said, "or in any event at least wait for your biopsy, its only next Wednesday."

The Tigers didn't come that night. The two of us went to a local Bistro for dinner, and a bottle of champagne and two liquor coffees helped me slip- almost immediately into a deep, but dream-filled sleep.

The dream began when I mixed up the two letters I written a few days early, and posted the one in which I had vented my spleen *(what an earth does that mean anyway)*. Somehow this resulted in my lying in theatre with a gowned up Mr Breading, Dr. Traynor, The Lovely Nita, The Receptionist from Oncology. And, strangely enough, the car park attendant who had told me on the day of my specialist DRE "You can only park here for 20 minutes sir". He was holding hands with the man with the white beard and the cheery smile.

"Right, nurse, what do we have here?"

"A new patient Doctor"

"My word," he said and I could see his smile through his mask, "I do believe that's Mr Jay. What's his problem?"

44

"Well Doctor, I do believe he has a rather troublesome spleen" said Nursie of the white plastic cup.

"He also parked in a 20 minute zone for 23 minutes" said the car park attendant brusquely. The man with the white beard gave me a cheery smile.

"A troublesome spleen," said Mr Breading," my my, we can't have that, now can we, we better have a look."

"What about the parking?" said the car park attendant

"Sod off" said Mr Breading,   "I've got a troublesome spleen on the table."

"There it is Doctor"

"So it is, a vented spleen if I ever saw one"

"Had we better cut it out Doctor?"

"Absolutely nurse, pass me that old Swiss army knife"

"This one Doctor?"

"That's the one, and that ball of string - now after three, one, two, three, there that's got it"

"Shall I throw it in the bin Doctor?"

"Goodness me no.....keep the spleen, throw Mr Jay in the bin."

"What about the parking?" said our friend

"Sod off" said Mr Breading

The man with the white beard gave me a cheery smile

CHAPTER 8
A COMFORTABLY
FULL BLADDER

JULY 2004

"Happy Birthday Darling" Polly was standing over me with a cup of coffee and a handful of colourful envelopes. I sat up in bed and took a well deserved kiss for reaching 62 with all my teeth. Well for reaching 62 anyway.

"Thank you very much" I said in the clipped tones the 'Scaffold' had used in their brilliant 1960's number 1 *"Thank you very much"* As was our family practice, I opened all the cards, and then sat back to receive my pressies. "You will have your birthday present later today" smiled Polly.

"What time *is* my biopsy?" I said, remembering. I picked up the appointment letter from the bedside table.

"Well?" asked Poll

"10 o'clock" I replied"

"Any special instructions?" she asked

"I have to go with" I glanced at the appointment letter " *a comfortably full bladder*" I mused. I could recall many times when my bladder could have been described as *uncomfortably full*.   I am sure that for the majority of my sleeping hours and most of my waking day my bladder felt *comfortably empty*.   I could not, however, think of a single moment when I had suddenly been struck with the notion that my bladder was *comfortably full*.

"Excuse me sir, is sir's bladder <u>comfortably full</u> or would sir like another Kir Royale?"

"Thank you waiter, perhaps just half a glass"

"How do you know when its '*comfortably full*'?" Polly asked

"Pass" I answered, realising that the answer was more appropriate to the next stage, that of *un-comfortably full,*

"Have a wee when you get up" said Polly, ever practical, "but then don't go again until after your biopsy.   That should fill the bill"

"Or at least fill the bladder" I thought.

We arrived at the hospital at about 9.45.   Polly pulled up at the short entrance drive and I climbed out.   She then set off to find a parking space, amidst and against, the seemingly thousands of cars that were flowing into the concreted acres of the hospital grounds.   I suspected her job would be more frustrating than mine.   I walked past the parking attendant whom I had last seen gowned up at the removal of my spleen.

He had obviously forgotten because he merely nodded good morning.

Once through the entrance doors, I made my way along the corridor. I had seen the 'Ultrasound' department on my previous visit. That was on the day of the white plastic cup. I went and sat down outside the door, knowing Polly would find me easily enough once she had parked the car. It did occur to me that I was the only man sitting on the row, and I pondered this new revelation that even some women have troublesome prostates. A nurse came up to me.

"Can I help you?" she asked with a lovely smile.

"I'm here for a scan" I spoke quietly.

"I hope not" she said, "this is ante natal"

"Ouch" I grimaced

"I expect you *want* a Transrectal" she said, did I imagine the excitement in the expectation that I *wanted* a Transrectal she expanded "a TRUS" she said, clearly implying just the ONE S.

One or two of the women looked up from their magazines in mild interest.

"That's right" I murmured

"Just follow the signs to X Ray," she said, "and check in at their reception" I thanked her, and limped off in the direction she indicated sure that several pairs of eyes were following my every limp.

When I eventually found the right department (which wasn't quite X Ray, although that department had been a useful staging post), It was five minutes past ten.

"I'm the late Mr Jay" I said, attempting a feeble joke

"The late?" queried the receptionist

"I should have been here five minutes ago" I said raising my eyebrows.

"Just a take a seat," she responded, "The nurse will come and see you."

I turned around and looked for the man with the badge and the white plastic cups. Not there, I was infused with rush of relief. I took in the room, much, much smaller that the heaving mass of prostate enlarged humanity I had encountered at my last visit. BUT, the man with white beard and the cheery smile was one of the number. He nodded at me as I caught his eye, I nodded back. The corner table was awash with magazines on the super-natural. *'I was captured by aliens'* *'Crop Circles, are they really an aliens plaything?'* *'I talked to Napoleon and played the piano with Beethoven.'* Weird choice, I thought, are they trying to prepare us for the *'other side.'* I thumbed through them anyway. I knew that Polly had still to negotiate, not only the car park, but the car park attendant and the ante-natal ultrasound and the route march through X Ray.

"Mr Jay" Napoleon was still only a blob in the corner of the magazine, but I tore my eyes from the promising page, and looked up. It was the nurse. "Will you come with me?" I smiled and looked around. The man with the white beard had gone, so had his cheery smile. She took me to a cubicle.

"Undress for me, and pop your things in the locker, pop on the gown and robe, pop your shoes back on and come back to the waiting room." She spoke slowly, as if to a foreigner. Why?, I wondered do you always 'POP' your shoes back on when you're in hospital, why don't you PUT them on like you do at home. Having undressed down to my socks, I slipped my arms through the gown. It was obviously the same one I wore last time, except that it had now shrunk in the wash. I tried to do up the lace behind my neck. It just reached, although a bow was impossible and I ended up with a knot that would probably never come undone. To tie any other lace was not even an option, but I was grateful for the robe which came as close to meeting at the front as the gown did at the back.

Nevertheless, between the two of them I was relatively well covered. I POPPED on my shoes, locked my 'things' in the locker and went to rejoin Napoleon. The man with the white beard was back. Dressed as I was though I suspected at a glance that his robe was a size smaller. His cheery smile had gone. He was reading Napoleon. I sat down and tried 'Crop Circles'. We were summoned together, and walked a few paces down a short corridor, he was shown into a room on the left, and I was led into a room on the right. The show, was about to start.

"Mr...........Jay" he paused, looked up, "Please sit down" I sat down.

"Your PSA was 12, it should be between 0.1 and 0.4," He waited as if to let the facts sink in. "It means we are definitely looking for cancer"

Thank you for those words of comfort, I thought

"I see" I said, and I did, I'd read that all sorts of other problems can increase a PSA reading, but he seemed in no mood to consider them, far less discuss.

"What is a Transrectal Ultrasound?" he said. Hang on one tiny minute, I thought, here's the guy whose going to perform one.......on me..... and he's asking *me* what it is. "Do you know?", he continued, and thankfully I realised that his question was rhetorical. "Do you know how one is Performed,?" I'd got the hang of it now.

"No" I said, confident that it was the correct answer.

"Well, I'm going to place a small, specially shaped probe in your rectum"

"I bet its finger shaped" I thought, memories of my DRE's flooding back

"That is so that I can see your prostate. You will find this a little uncomfortable, but it *shouldn't* be painful" I didn't like the slight emphasis on the *shouldn't*. I will then use the ultrasound to guide a small needle into the gland through the wall of the rectum, and take tissue samples" He looked at me expectantly, no doubt expecting questions...I had none. "I will give you an antibiotic to reduce the risk of infection, I will also give you a local anaesthetic immediately before the biopsy" I still had no questions, to fill the gap I wondered about asking whether I would have to face the wall, but that seemed a little too frivolous.

"During the biopsy I will take several small samples of tissue" I later learned that he had taken NINE. "When each sample is taken the needle makes a loud snapping noise. Don't worry about this" Who's worried?,

"It is perfectly normal and won't hurt you. I'll then give you a further antibiotic suppository in your back passage."

"I understand," I said

"Finally I will want you to empty your bladder just to ensure that you are well" At last, my *comfortably full bladder* was coming into its own.

"There will be a little blood, but that is quite normal"

"Oh for how long?" I asked

"About a fortnight" he said, "Any questions?"

"No", but thank you for a very full explanation

"Right, jump up on the couch", jumping, I thought, has got to be better than POPPING.

"Good, now just lay on your side, draw your knees up to your chest, and FACE THE WALL"

"Half an hour, or was it half a lifetime later when I had counted every crack and blemish on a boringly white wall, as well as every crack of the probing needle. he spoke. "Good" he said, "that was fine." I was, of course, delighted that at least one of us had had a good time.

"I would just like you to have a little pee." *My comfortably full bladder* had felt anything but *comfortably full* for some time, "if there are no problems you can get dressed and 'pop' off' " I was past caring. The nurse led me to a door.

"Can you 'pop' " (that word again) "in there and do a little wee for me?"

Now come on; a fifty something woman, asking a sixty something man, "can you pop in here and do a little wee for me." I popped in there and did a little wee for her. It looked OK to me although it was a decidedly deep red, "That's fine" she said, you can get dressed now and doctor will send your results to Oncology."

And so, with a happy nurse behind me, I *Popped* into the cubicle, *Popped* my key into the locker, *Popped* my robe onto the hook, *Popped* my Gown on to the floor. *Popped* my shoes onto my feet, and *Popped* out of the Hospital to find Polly. She was still in Ante-Natal. We were both relieved that neither a brother or a sister for our thirty-something children had *Popped* out anywhere in the interim.

"There you are" she said,
"Here I am" I answered
"How do you feel?" she said
"I'm alright" I answered
"What would you like to do now?" she asked, I thought for a second

"Can we just POP off home?". I said.

I scrunched up on the comfy sofa in the conservatory.   I was not exactly in pain, but I was - how had the Doctor described it - uncomfortable. A dozen times in an hour I tried to *do a little wee for the nurse'*, without success, desperate but incapable. The need was there, the ability wasn't. The day passed, the water didn't.

I missed lunch, and dozed in the afternoon sun.   After all, it was my birthday.   By mid-afternoon I was feeling quite chirpy.   At around 4 o'clock, Polly said - "we're going out for a really nice birthday dinner to-night" I knew I deserved it, after-all, hadn't I been a brave little soldier.

"Where are we going?" I asked

"I'm not telling you" she said

"What time are we leaving?" I said planning a long soaking bath and knowing exactly what hot water can do to a reluctant member, and how after (not during) *doing a little wee for the nurse"* would be a doddle.

"Now" she said

"It's only 4 o'clock" I said

"Now" she said

"When are we eating?" I asked

"No more questions" she said "it's a special surprise" And it was.

I was dressed simply in my usual 'day at the hospital' outfit.   Polly, always looks elegant, but when we are going somewhere special she does special things like combing *my* hair, and picking the bits of fluff off *my* pyjamas. So, here we are, 4.30 in the afternoon, dressed for a casual Bar-B-Q, and heading out for a special birthday treat.   I should have twigged, that it was going to be more than just a birthday dinner, but lets be straight, when you have spent half the morning facing the wall with a specially shaped, or come to that an ANY SHAPED, probe up your rectum, the mental processes DO slow down.   As we drove I ticked off the places we were not going, mainly on account of the fact that we were actually driving past them.   As the miles sped beneath the wheels, only one place remained, and even though I had been a brave little soldier, we could not possibly be going there.

About a half an hour drive from us there is a very special Country House Restaurant - for a week-end meal you need to reserve a table at least 2 months in advance.   In addition to being a fine, mega-demand restaurant, this Country House Restaurant has a few, very special Country House Rooms,

At 6 o'clock I was drinking Kir Royals on the Terrace.

At 7 o'clock I was luxuriating in an oversized bath, too good to test my earlier theory and anyway the nurses strange desires were already fading from my memory.

At 8 o'clock we were enjoying aperitifs in the bar.

At 9 o'clock we were deeply into the sort of menu I love, in surroundings I adore, fine linen tablecloths with fine linen napkins simply rolled, and contained within silver napkin rings. - wonderful food, and a champagne list to drool over.

At 10 o'clock we were enjoying a superb selection of cheeses and liqueurs.

At 11 o'clock we mellowed with coffee and petite fours in the lounge followed by night caps on the terrace.

At 12 o'clock..........well, at 12 o'clock my birthday treat continued.

THE TIGERS DIDN'T COME THAT NIGHT

CHAPTER 9
IT'S ONLY TITCHY

JULY 2004

I had resigned myself to a longish wait between my birthday biopsy and the end of August results clinic. We returned from our splendid over-nighter, and settled into a mild routine. Polly played golf each Monday - beautifully. I played golf each Thursday - pathetically. We ate out every other night and every lunch-time. The weather, whilst not providing the idyllic English summer, was OK, and we coasted along.

The nightly vehemence of my Tigers was inversely proportionate to the quality (and I suppose quantity) of the evening's champagne. Most nights they would visit. And, it has to be said, each night one would always be more dominant than the others.

'Resignation' whose name could also be 'Passive Acceptance' was usually the first on the scene.   *"Relax,"* he would say, *"you've done all you can, another day has passed, it will be the end of August before you know it, and the waiting will be over.   No point in getting agitated, there is nothing you can do but wait."*

'Fear' *it has to be said, was always ready to put in a bad word, but in these passing days of early August, his voice was lost beside the others.*

It was around the middle of the month when I got the phone call.

"Mr Jay?"

"Yes"

"It's Lynn here, Lynn from the surgery"

"Oh, Hello Lynn, this is a surprise"

"Dr. Hakelin wonders if you could pop in and see her?"

"Oh, I see, when"

"Could you manage about 5 o'clock?"   It was De Ja Vu............ all over again.

"Hello Basil"

"Hello Doctor, Doctor, do you mind if I call you Nita?" she hesitated,

"No" she said, "I don't mind."

"It's positive, but its really titchy." she said holding her thumb and forefinger about half an inch apart.   I wasn't immediately on her wave-length, and it obviously showed in my furrowed brow. Recognising my blank stare she smiled.   "I have the result of your biopsy"

"AAAHHH" I said, my face lighting up with comprehension.

"Its Bad News, and it's Good News" she said in capital letters.

"The Bad News is that you have Cancer, but" she paused for effect,

"The Good News is that it's Titchy".   At that point, wanting to share some of the responsibility, I held up my hand with my thumb and forefinger a half inch apart.

"Titchy" I said,

"Titchy" she repeated, "and what's more, it doesn't appear to have spread."

She went on to explain that they had taken NINE biopsy samples, but that only THREE of them showed Cancer.   No, she didn't know what grade it was.   No, she didn't know its staging.   No, she couldn't, or at least she shouldn't, attempt to second-guess the treatment that Mr Breading would recommend.   She just couldn't bear the thought of me having to tough it out until the end of August not knowing, when she had a copy of the report.   I thanked her, I told her she was a star, and I walked out of the surgery and down the street with a lighter step than for several weeks.

The Tigers still came, in that pre-dawn period when even the birds are still asleep, no doubt battling their own 'tigers.'

'Hope' always led the parade with his *I told you everything would be fine.*

'Fear' tried to spoil it by reminding me that, *"OK, its only Titchy, and it hasn't spread.   BUT YOU STILL HAVE BLOODY CANCER."*

CHAPTER 10
A CHINESE TALE

AUGUST 2004

On looking back over the summer of 2004 I will remember, amongst other things, some remarkable 'ups' that more than compensated for the occasional 'downs'.   Oddly enough, one of the major 'DOWNS' had also been one of the most uplifting 'UPS'.   Let me explain.

I am very proud of my wife's golfing achievements.   She and I both enjoy playing golf, and indeed play a lot of our golf together.   BUT, it has to be said, she has a spirit of competition that has long since left me as far as the golf course is concerned.   Now it also has to be said.   She hasn't got the willowy swing of Ernie Els, nor the cool temperament of Tiger Woods.   She doesn't jump and fizz around the course like Sergio Garcia, and when it comes to smoking fat cigars and drinking Guinness she cannot hold a candle to

Darren Clarke.   But, she is straight, she is reliable and she is calm.   These were the attributes that enabled her to win the club's monthly medal that led to the most exciting time either of us have ever spent - on a golf course.   On the day of the monthly medal, Polly had paid an extra £1 to enter a national competition.   The Ladies Amateur Golf Championship of Great Britain and Ireland.   As already mentioned, she won her monthly medal with a net 67, and this gave her a place in the Regional Finals.   26,000 ladies had entered the competition, and just 900 were going forward.   There were a choice of 16 Regional venue's throughout Great Britain.   Polly chose to play her Regional, which was to be held in early August, on a course she had never played before. *Eastbourne DOWNS Golf Club.*   It is in *Eastbourne*, it is on the *Downs*, and of course it is a *golf club*.   Clever play on words really.   Be that as it may, the fact is she won this Regional Final with 37 points and found herself, just one of sixteen, in the National Final which was to be played on the famous Wentworth West Course at the end of September.   So, as you can see, one of my major DOWNS, was also, by a country mile, one of the most wonderful UPS of my curious year.   I know, cut out the jokes and stick to the doom and gloom narrative.   But therein, you see, lies the problem.,   However BAD the news, it is impossible to maintain a doom and gloom face for long.   Life is so full of so many wonderfully unexpected moments that lift your spirits and your hopes. My wife's golfing success in the summer of 2004 was most definitely one of them.

Early in August I had another. Polly had arranged a week-end in Deauville, that splendid coastal French town so beloved of the wealthy, race-going gentry of nineteenth century England. Polly and I had discovered Deauville, and more particularly *The Hotel de Golf*, in the early 1990's. A bit of *'old world class'* at *'new world money.'* But come on, if you don't spoil *yourself* once in a while, time sure as hell will.

We spent a wonderful week-end, the sun shone from it's rise to it's set. It shone on the pool, it shone on the surrounding eucalyptus trees, it shone on the colourful parasols, and it most certainly shone on me. Young, Jack, all 18 months of him took to the water like the duck (forgive the cockney) he is. He is, of course, a young man set on a multi-lingual road. His mother (my daughter) is married to a splendidly humorous young man from Yorkshire However, they both met in Paris where they have lived for the past 15 years. Consequently young Jack lives in a bi-lingual environment, and in addition has a grand-pappy (me) who can order champagne in a least half a dozen languages . I didn't want that week-end to end. Of course, the Tigers came, but I told them to bugger off and wait until I got back home.

As the month progressed we were engulfed in various other wonderful events. One day the chimney sweep came. On another day our shower packed up and we had to call the plumber. In the middle of the month I had a dental appointment, but me - ha - I laugh in the face of adversity (and dentists since I had my implants).

I am afraid that I must now re-introduce my A.R.F. It is important to the story because, you see, it wasn't getting any better. Although I was sure dear old Mufi, who really was a delightful man, cried a little tear every time he saw me limp by his office on my way to the digital administrations of others (or am I kidding myself). One day, Polly and I were whiling away an hour or two between lunch-time Kir Royale and evening Champagne cocktails. We drove to Bluewater, one of the biggest shopping malls in the South of England., During our aimless wandering, I stumbled (that bloody foot again) upon a sign which read. *ACUPUNCTURE CAN CURE YOUR ARTHITIS.* Had fate, who had dealt me a bit of a bum hand this summer, decided to offer me a crumb and led me to the door of *THE CHINESE MEDICINE CENTRE* . Was it offering me a fully functioning foot in return for a prune shaped prostate. Only time, and the delightful modern day Suzie Wong who stood there smiling at me, could give me the answer.

I would have walked away, (Polly already had), but then the smiling Suzie, put her hands together, came and stood close do me, gave a funny little bow, and, disappointingly, instead of saying "AH SO," said "Is there some way we can help sir?" I looked at her.   Yes, there was definitely someway she could help me, but I put it out of my mind.   I remembered what my paternal grandmother used to say to me.

"If wishes were pomegranates, elephants would be ten feet tall".   No I don't know what it means either.   Instead I said

"Do you sell lollipops?"

"Rorripops" she said.   I had always wanted to do that.

"Sorry" I said

"It aw wite" she might have said - but didn't

"I've got arthritis in my right foot" I said.

"Ah So" she didn't say - these girls never play to the script.   "Dr Liu Meong (or was in Meong Liu) will help you" she said.   "Come in and let me register you"   I went in and let her register me.

"Please that is £10" she said

"What is £10?" I asked.

"To be registered" she said

"What do I get for £10?" I wanted to know

"Registration" she said.   I gave her £10

 "Now what?" I said.

"Dr Meong Liu" (or was it Liu Meong)   "will examine you, please sit here".   I sat there.   After about five minutes Suzie was back.   "Dr Liu Meong" (or was in Meong Liu) "will see you now, please to follow me".   I remembered rorripops and wondered why she didn't say forrow me.   Then I realized - she had my £10 now - inscrutable these Chinese. She led me into a small curtained cubicle with Chinese patterned wallpaper, a deep rosewood desk and chairs, and a framed Chinese Motto which read "♍︎♒︎   ♏︎⟋◆︎♓︎◆︎⟋   ◆︎⟋🝰☉◆︎ ◆︎♏︎⟋🝰🝰◆︎♓︎&🝰♏︎" I reflected that it probably translated to *"A fool and his £10 are soon parted - and you don't even get a rorripop"* Frank Sinatra sang softly in Chinese from a speaker in the corner. The Doctor smiled.

"◆︎◆︎   ◆︎   ◆︎♓︎◆︎   ♑︎◆︎🝰♑︎♑︎🝰🝰🝰⟋♏︎♑︎♒︎ 🝰✞🝰✂︎✂︎" He said

"The Doctor, say Herro" said Suzie.

"Hello Doctor" I said, "How am I?" then I remembered its reception in English and cringed.

"❖♓︎   ◆︎♑︎🝰   ♓︎♑︎♍︎♏︎♑︎⟋◆︎♓︎♓︎♒︎☻✞✞🝰 ♒︎☻   ◆︎♏︎⟋♓︎   ☹✞   ☺✞   ♓︎✞🝰🝰✞   ☞☺🝰♓︎◆︎ ⟋   ♓︎◆︎♏︎⟋🝰♓︎◆︎♏︎◆︎   ♓︎◆︎"

"Doctor thin that velly funny" said Suzie.   I smiled realizing that what he had probably said was,

"Where *do* you get them from Suzie, another one who thinks he's Wonnie Corbett".   The Doctor took my wrist and felt my pulse with three fingers.

"♓︎♑︎◆︎♏︎◆︎⟋♓︎♏︎&🝰   ♑︎♏︎🝰⟋   ◆︎✞♒︎🝰🝰   ♒︎   🝰◆︎✞☞♏︎♓︎♒︎🝰   ✋✞♏︎◆︎⟋♓︎🝰🝰♏︎◆︎☞☺   🝰♓︎✞◆︎♏︎♓︎⟋🝰◆︎♓︎🝰🝰✞♓︎🝰   ✋☺🝰✞☞ ♓︎✋🝰✞◆︎♏︎⟋♓︎♓︎◆︎✡🝰✞☞🝰✋🝰♓︎✡✋🝰🝰🝰   ⟋❖♑︎♓︎♓︎🝰♏︎◆︎⟋◆︎♓︎♓︎🝰✞   ☞♐♓︎✋◆︎ ◆︎⟋♓︎♓︎✞🝰🝰✋♓︎   ♓︎◆︎♓︎♑︎◆︎♏︎   ⟋◆︎♑︎♓︎♓︎✞🝰☞ ☞♓︎✋◆︎   ◆︎♏︎⟋♓︎♓︎♓︎"

"Doctor say you have other probrem as well as arthritis, he feel pulse on three levels."

"I have a prostate problem" I said

"He know" she said

"❖□ ▭ ❑◆ ♓■♑□♐♓♏⬥♐ ♊♓■☜☞♱✋ ⬥♓♏♊♐◆ ♊♓♏⬥♐◆⍓❖♓■♊⌖✡☜☞✋⚐♊⍓⬥◆♏ ♐ ♓■♱☜☞♊◆♏⬥♐♊■♓♱☜⌖☞⚐◆⍓♏⬥♐❖ ♓■◆⬥☜♊☞♱☜⌖☞ ☯♊♱⬥❖◆♊☯⌖☜♱☞♱ ♊⚐♏◆⬥ ♐♊♓■☯✋♱♊✋☯◆♏⬥♊"

"But Doctor say that not all, you have heart missing beat and this could be nallow archery"

"Nallow archery?" I said

"Nallow archery" she repeated "maybe too much krestral - he say you go to Doctor for Eazy Gee".

The penny dropped, Narrow Artery, ECG. Thank you fate, I mouthed, and I thought this summer was going to be boring. "Doctor would like to start on your arthritis today, but he say you must see Doctor about other things".

"Thank Doctor Meong Liu" (or was it Liu Meong) "for his advice" I said.

"♎❖□ ♊♋ ♏&▭ ♏⬥♊□▭ ◆♏□▭♊ ♓♊ ♓♏⬥ ♊"

"Doctor say you velly welcome."

"What does Doctor want to do to my foot,"

"♎♐❖ &♊♋ ❒♑♓■ ❑ ♊ ♓ ■ ❒ ♏ ♑ ◆ ♐ ♓ □ ⬥ ॐ ♏ ◆ ♐ ♓ ■ ♊ ⌖ ✡ ☜ ✌ ☞ ✋ ⚐ ✠ ✈ ✡ ☼ ☜ ✌ ⚐ ✡ ✠ ⚐ ✌ ☜ ♱ ⚐ ✈ ♱ ☜ ✌ ☼ ⚐✠✋♱✡☜⌖☞✋⚐✠✡☜⌖♱✌☞⚐"

"He want to give you acupuncture first"

" &♏♐ &♍❑ ♐♏♊♏⬥♐&●♏⬥"

"Then he give you acupressure treatment, velly good"

"Ah so" I said, "far so good" I added not wanting a man who was about to stick needles in me thinking I was extracting the Michael.

"Then we give you special Chinese Herbs for you to boil your feet"

"Good job there's nothing wrong with my head" I said.

"⬜ ⯑⯑⯑⯑⯑⯑ ⯑⬜ ⬜⯑⯑⯑⯑⯑⬜⬜◆⬜⯑◆⬜⯑ ⯑⬜⬜⯑⯑◆⯑⬜☻ " laughed the Doctor.

"Good job" said Suzie Wong

"⯑◆❖ ⯑⯑⯑ ⯑ ⯑⯑⬜ ⯑❖⬜⯑⯑ ◆❖◆⯑◆⯑❖⯑✕" said the Doctor.

"Then he give you oitment to wub in evley day"

"Wub in evley day?" I questioned.

"Evley day, wub in" repeated Suzie as if I'd find it easier the other way around.

"⯑ ⯑⯑⯑⯑⯑⯑⯑ ⬜⯑⬜⯑⯑⯑⯑⬜" said the Doctor.

"Ah so", I said, nobody laughed this time. I was conscious of Polly still wandering about outside. She had not followed me into Suzie Wong's den, and probably thought that I was on my third hokey cokey pipe, whilst half a dozen Suzie Wong's walked up and down my spine wearing nothing but designer wellies. Dream on Basil.

"How long does the treatment last?" I asked

"The acupuncture twenty minute" said Suzie forgetting the S, "the acupressure 15 minute"

"And how much is the treatment?", I asked.

"Acupuncture 25 pynd a session" she said, "and Acupressure 35 pynd, but" she added quickly seeing my raised eyebrows," for special people with acupuncture and acupressure together, velly special price"

"How velly special?" I asked

"Instead of 60 pynd " she said "we do 40 pynd"

"Sounds expensive I thought, and then I remembered Mufi's 3,500 pynds plus VAT and I was still limping.

"Let me find my wife and tell her how long I will be" I said. "Just put on the wellies," I thought, "I'll be back in a minute."

Polly expressed relative contentment to a further 45 minute walk-about, but then she seldom expresses annoyance, irritation or exasperation anyway - I must be pretty easy to live with. I went back inside and was shown into a different cubicle with a different Chinese legend on the wall but the same Frank Sinatra was still climbing out of the speaker. There was a nallow couch against the wall, and small rosewood table and chair in the corner.

"Take of shoes and socks and lie on couch" said Suzie. I waited for the *and just face the wall* - instead she said. "good, you lie back and weelax, Doctor Meong Liu" (or was it Liu Meong) "will see you shortly". Frank Sinatra was quietly warbling *Mi Wei* from the speaker above my head. Things, like me, were certainly looking up.

Who said acupuncture was painless. The Doctor came in through the curtains like a stage magician. I soon discovered he was 'four words fluent' in English. *Weddy, Pain, Hugh and Weelax.* He used them constantly. He smiled. I smiled back. He rolled up my trouser leg. He put on a latex glove. His smile never faltered and I had to push to the back of my memory the last time a Doctor had put on a latex glove in my presence. "Weddy?" he said

"Absolutely" I said as he pushed a long needle into my leg just below the knee. I felt a mild pricking sensation. This was going to be OK. He slid another needle into my leg half way between the ankle and the little clump of black hairs that for some reason grow more thickly there than anywhere else. The same mild pricking sensation.

"Weddy?" he said again

"Weddy" I repeated followed by "BLOODY ADA" at 100 decibels above the acceptable norm. He had pushed the third needle into the middle of my operation scar. I scrunched my toes tight and straightened my leg as in a spasm of cramp.

"Pain?" said The Doctor "Hugh?"

"Yes" I gasped, wondering who the hell Hugh was,

"Weelax" he said "Weddy?"

"OK" I whispered, determined not to be so wimpy again now that I knew what was coming. Three more needles went into the scar, each time a pain shot up my leg, each time he soothingly chanted in an hypnotic, sing song voice.

"Pain, Hugh, Weelax.....Weddy. Pain, Hugh, Weelax....Weddy" The final two needles painlessly slid into the top of my foot several inches away from my scar. Doctor Meong Liu (or was it Liu Meong) added an additional "Weelax", and disappeared in a swirl of curtain., Frank Sinatra was asking Joe to *'Set 'em up'* , because, after all, according to old Frankie, It was *'3 o'clock in the morning.'*

Once the needle wielding Doctor had gone taking his smile and my pain with him, I felt strangely calm. So calm that even Frank Sinatra, who now appeared to be on the *'Woad to Mandaray'* became bearable. I lay back and closed my eyes. Somebody snoring woke me up. It was me. About half an hour passed, the curtain twitched and Suzie Wong's head appeared, then disappeared. It was followed immediately by Doctor Liu Meong (or was it..........) What he did to me next was clearly a well planned revenge for our capture of Singapore three hundred years earlier. After he had painlessly removed the 8 needles, he began to press and to pound my ankle, digging his fingers deep into my scar, The pain was intense, and the smile never left his face, as he got into his stride and his hypnotic chant.

"Weelax, Pain?, Hugh?, Weddy?, Weelax, Pain?, Hugh?, Weddy?, Weelax............" I tried to close my mind to everything except Frank Sinatra....but that was painful as well.   Eventually it was over. The Doctor swirled away and Suzie swirled in.

"That hurt" I said to her.

"Doctor must make blood flow through joint again, why pain" she said.

"I see" I said, thinking I better learn a little about this tortuous treatment. "Do you have any books on Chinese medicine?" I asked.

"Try Waterstones" she said. I did, they had. Back in the shop Suzie had weighed me out seven bags of noxious weed. "Put in large saucepan" she said, "add water, soak for 15 minute" she said "Bring to boil and simmer for 30 minute" she said. Please don't ask me to drink it I thought "Do I drink it?" I asked.   Suzie laughed.

"You drink, you get bad stomach" she said. "You soak you feet in it twice a day for 40 minute."

"Ah so" I said - "is it time for the arithmetic"

"riffmatic" she said

"What do I owe you?" I said.   She smiled.

"Normal price" she say "60 pynd - ten sessions 600 pynd"   I was streets ahead of her with the riffmatic.   "For you velly special price 40 pynd session, ten session 400 pynd".   She looked at me to make sure I understood.

"Ah so" I could have said, but didn't "OK" I said instead.

"Velly special Chinese Herbs 200 pynd - 30 day supply.   Charge you 170 pynd   Doctor say you must clean blood with velly special Green Tea, only 50 pynd 100 bags. Total 620 pynd." I felt like she was sticking needles in my wallet.

I gave her my credit card.   As I walked away Suzie called after me.   "Don't forget boil your feet".   I smiled, thinking that after all I would probably have done better to boil my head.

Tania, Nigel and little Jack came to stay with us for the week-end.   Tim and Virve (my eldest son and his partner - shortly to become is wife) joined us as did my youngest son Jeremy, who flew in from Tenerife for a long week-end.   I collected my mother from Eastbourne so that we could have a quiet family dinner party.   The boys and I stayed up until gone five in the morning drinking chatting, and cultivating a suitably debilitating headache for the following day.   No-one except Polly knows about my cancer.   We have decided to keep it that way until we have the final results and know the treatment.

I went to see Suzie Wong, and Doctor Liu Meong (or is it Meong Liu) eight times during August but the *'designer welly'* fantasy remained just that.   I am sure that the foot felt easier.

I had no fear of August 31st and the results clinic.   After all, hasn't the lovely Nita already explained.   IT'S TITCHY AND IT HASN'T SPREAD.

CHAPTER 11
A BAD BEGINNING EXPLAINED

AUGUST 2004

It was August 31st.   A day I had not been looking forward to.   Even the very name 'results clinic' conjures up bad news.   However, for me, it was to be a doddle.

Thanks to the lovely Nita, I knew the worst.   I had cancer. *BUT IT WAS TITCHY.*   She didn't know the grade.   *BUT IT HADN'T SPREAD.*
What else was there to know?

Polly wanted to come with me, but she had the opportunity to play in a golf match, and I wasn't going to be getting bad news was I, so what was the point in her missing a good outing of golf to sit in a hospital waiting room with me for an hour or so when I knew. *IT WAS TITCHY, AND IT HADN'T SPREAD.*
I did forget one thing, and that was that I had to park the car.   I also cut it a bit fine so I was

five minutes late by the time I had found a parking space, abused the car park attendant (I'd never forgiven him for assisting at my spleen operation) and reached reception.   I dispensed with the 'late Mr Jay' joke.

"Mr Jay for Mr Breading" I said

"Mr Breading is on leave" said the receptionist, "you will be seeing Dr Postern"

"Right" I said

I looked around, not a lot had changed.   The man with the badge and the trolley was on station, white plastic cups at the ready.   The man with the white beard and the cheery smile wasn't there.   Perhaps they had stuck with his original appointment or put him off till 2029.

"Take a seat" she said "and the nurse will ignore you"...she didn't really say that, although it would probably have been accurate.   But it wasn't, it was a different nurse.   She didn't ignore me, she didn't thrust a plastic cup in my hand, she didn't ask me to fill in a form.   She did say.

"Mr Jay, good morning, have you had your bone scan and MRI?"   I looked at her blankly - the old joke of "stop looking at my blankly" came into my head but was chased out by incomprehension of the question I had just been asked.

"No," I said, "I don't think that's me" I was sure there must be another Mr. Jay, "I'm just here to get the results of my biopsy" *ITS TITCHY, AND IT HASN'T SPREAD....The lovely Nita TOLD me,* rang in my brain

"That's, alright, just checking, the doctor won't be long."   Now what was all that about. Bone scan, MRI whatever that is, what on earth has that got to do with a prune shaped prostate, particularly when *IT'S TITCHY, AND IT HASN'T SPREAD*.

"Mr Jay" I looked up, she was smiling, I waited for her to say "sorry about that, wrong Mr Jay" she didn't, she did say "Dr Postern is ready for you now.   I walked straight into room 8, a regular now.   I did not pass cubicle, I did not take of my trousers, I did not struggle into an undersized gown, and I knew I would not have to 'Face the Wall' I was just going to sit there and be told, "Mr Jay, you have cancer, but its titchy and it hasn't spread."

"Well Mr Jay" he said, "You've got cancer" he said

"Oh," I said, "Yeah, Yeah, Yeah", I thought, *BUT ITS TITCHY, AND IT HASN'T SPREAD, The Lovely Nita TOLD me.*

"It's High Grade" he said "That means its aggressive" he said

"Oh" I said, *BUT ITS TITCHY, AND* IT HASN'T SPREAD, The lovely Nita TOLD me.

"We are not convinced that it has not already spread to the bones and perhaps the surrounding tissue" he said

"Oh" I said, *BUT ITS TITCHY, AND IT HASN'T SPREAD, The lovely Nita TOLD ME.*

"We have arranged for you to have a full body scan, and an MRI scan of the pelvic and abdominal regions" he said

"Oh" I said, then, finding my voice developed the theme "When will that.......?"

"Dr. MacDermot will write to you" he interrupted

"Oh" I said "How soo.......?"

"Dr MacDermot will contact you", he tidied his papers

"Yes, but I wou..........?"

"I'm sure Dr McDermot will treat it as priority" he interrupted again

He leaned on his desk and half raised himself, as if to get up.   The consultation was clearly over. *BUT IT'S ONLY TITCHY, AND IT HASN'T SPREAD.* I wanted to tell him.   *BUT IT'S ONLY TITCHY, AND IT HASN'T SPREAD.* I yelled inside my mind.

"Thank you" I said, and, climbing down off my chair, I scurried across the floor, crept under the door, and out of his office, a 62 year old man, reduced to less than 2 inches tall by a doctor not long out of short trousers. I walked numbly along the busy corridor, it was full of people, but I was quite alone.   This wasn't me, I'm not normally 'fobbed' off without having my say. I can send back a tough steak with the best of them. But then again, the threat of bone devouring cancer may be tough titty, but it is definitely in a different league to a tough steak.

I walked out of the sombre dark cool of the hospital and into a bright and cheerful day.   The sun was shining.   But it wasn't shining for me.

It was August 31st 2004.

HAVE YOU HEARD A TIGER ROAR.

It seemed early when the Tigers came that night.

'Fear' was over the moon

What did I tell you", he said. "Rampant, that's what it is, bloody rampant.

You've heard the stories at the Golf Club , 'What about poor old Bill?, felt under the weather and went to see the quack.   That was June, poor old bugger was dead by September.' " I didn't want to listen, but his voice was pretty loud and pretty insistent.

'Hope' was keen to interrupt

"Don't listen. Dr Postern is just making sure, and there's nothing wrong with that. There won't be anything wrong with the scans.   Remember what you were told last time.   You have none of the symptoms. I reckon They were a bit surprised it was cancer.   Nah, definitely nothing to worry about. Anyway, you're only 62, plenty of life in you yet".

'Fear' was back like a shot.

"62, what's that got to do with the price of cheese.   George Harrison was 58, John Thaw was 63. Paul Eddington was 63 and poor old Bobby

Moore was only 55.   And what about Cilla Blacks husband, Bobby Willis wasn't it?' he was under 60.   Old Ronnie Wood of the Rolling Stones is suffering from it at the moment, and the great Rock Star Johnny Ramone, died last week at 57., You're not special, why should it get all them and give you a get out of jail card eh!! EH!!

'Regret' had something to say.
"Why didn't you go private when you said you would?   You have lost at least 4 weeks by waiting. Those four weeks could be vital.   You should have gone private when you first got riled up about the cancelled appointment.

I hadn't seen 'Resignation' for a while, but he was here now.
"Look," he said.   "You'd like another 20 years, so what, if you've got to go, you've got to go. You've been bloody lucky.   You've had 62 years that millions of people would pluck out an eye for. You've never been poor, admittedly there has been a time or two when the bones of your backside have appeared to be a bit close to the ground, but you were through all of that by the time you were 40.   You've had no real tragedy in your life.

Your poor old dad died when he was 29, and you were just a nipper, but in a perverse way that was your mum's tragedy rather than yours.   You didn't feel the pain of grief from losing a loved one, what you felt was the duller grief of missing something you knew should have been there as you grew up, but that hole in your life was always so

78

lovingly filled by a wonderful mother and others who cared about your 'growing up' years.

You had childhood summers straight out of Enid Blyton, idylic and interminable summer days spent on golden sands. Even your boyhood pals had Enid Blyton names. Ginger Jack, Ronnie Seager, Vod Watkins, Jimmy Stean. Growing up was a long and pleasurable business - and after that things only got better. You were there during the magic sixties when you met Polly. Your own family have always been so close and loving.

Admittedly you had to deal with the usually growing pains of teenagers, and some of them tried you more than others. BUT, you all got through it, and now you have three children to be proud of, and a grandchild to love to bits. If you _have_ to go you will have so many things in the old memory box. The Indian trip. The big house. The boat in the South of France. The holiday home in the sun. The Jaguars, and even the Rolls Royce. The fun of being at the cutting edge of a small town's hierarchy. And most important of all, a wife who has stood by you, and strangely enough, seemingly loved you for over 40 years., A pretty good life I'd say. To want more is normal, to expect more is just plain, bloody greedy.

I chose to go to sleep with the words of 'Resignation' ringing in my ears.

CHAPTER 12
THEM THAR BONES

AUGUST 2004

Polly and I hadn't discussed at any great lengths Dr Postern's delivered prognosis.   I had tried not to let the mind numbing possibilities get between me and a gentle evening spent in a favourite restaurant, a restaurant where we could, to some extent, face my Tigers in the open and together. Together, as we had faced so many things, good and not so good, during the 40 plus years of our shared life.

When Polly had arrived home from golf, I was sitting in the conservatory listening to Peter Katin playing Rachmaninov's 3rd Piano Concerto, a priceless recording with Sir Adrian Boult conducting the London Philharmonic.   Peter Katin was the very first concert pianist I ever saw play 'live'.   It was at the Winter Gardens in Margate.   I couldn't have been more than 10 years old and my dear mother had taken me for a very special treat   It was in the days I had vaguely hoped and my mother had been absolutely certain, that one day my musical abilities would match my musical desires.   Sadly they never did. In fact, my musical talent never ever came within a country mile of my musical aspirations. Peter Katin had played Rachmaninov that day - and it is still a work that I find almost unbearably emotional through its haunting melodies and its equally haunting memories. It certainly brought me closer to tears as I sat awaiting Polly's return than even Dr Postern's news had. Or perhaps it was a combination of the two coupled with the final realization that I would never play the piece of music, written in 1909 and generally accepted as being the most technically difficult of all the great piano works. Hell, even, my days of playing chopsticks or three blind mice could now be seriously in doubt.

"How did you get on?", I asked as Polly walked into the room.

"O.K. she said, how did YOU get on?"

"Not very well actually" she stood there, surprised, and waiting , I expanded a little, and inevitably, as you do, found a few inconsequential opening words.

"Mr Breading is still on leave"

"Who did you see?"

"One of his team, a man called Dr Postern"

"What was he like?"

"A bit abrupt, made me feel about two feet tall"

"What did he say?"

"Well, he talked about a multi-discipline meeting they have every Monday. Apparently they discuss a selection of current cases and take the views of all the department heads present on each case before discussing treatment options. Last Monday I was brought up"

"And"

"Apparently the pathologist"

"He'll be the doctor who carried out the biopsy"

"I suppose so, either carried it out or tested the sample", I said, "anyway, he has assessed the cancer as High Grade, which means very Aggressive" .... I paused "and apparently he is not convinced that it hasn't already spread to the bones and the surrounding tissue."

I still cannot believe how calmly I delivered this piece of news.....news that had had me driving home from the hospital just an hour or two earlier and not remembering a single yard of the journey.

"They want me to have a full body bone scan, and an MRI scan of the pelvic and abdominal regions." Polly, thank the Lord, has never been given to hysterics or over-reaction.

"When?" she said

"I don't know, the Doctor simply said that a Dr McDermot would be writing to me. I think that now is the time to go private, BUT, I have decided to go and see 'the lovely Nita' first and see what she thinks.

"That's a good idea," said Polly "I will phone her first thing in the morning and make an appointment"

"Since they changed their appointments process to an 'only on the day' system, I think it would be better if I went to the surgery. The last time you tried to phone at 8.o'clock in the morning, you didn't get through until ten-to-nine, and by then the only appointments left were early Evening."

"That's true" said Polly, "everyone has the same idea and all you get is that wretched *'our call is important to us, BUT YOU'RE IN A QUEUE"* Message."

"Absolutely, and I don't think I can wait all day tomorrow without taking some action. I thought I might get myself out of bed and be standing on the doorstep when they open the surgery doors. They obviously deal with patients at the counter before patients on the 'phone". The decision was made, there was no more to be said - at least for moment.

The place we held our very best post mortems, the venue for our most important *'and what are we going to do now'* discussions. The only place to tackle the big questions of life was a good restaurant. The best companions to join us were always a couple of Kir Royale's and a half bottle of Chablis. We were faced with a potential crisis we had never had to face before - not once in 40 years of being together. Two-thirds of our life had been spent sharing problems, sharing decisions. We had shared a young married's *'poverty.'* We had shared our children's growing pains. When they were teenagers we had shared their rebellions. We had shared their successes, we had shared their failures.

We had shared the happiness and joys of their first loves, and we had shared the sadness and despair of their first heartbreaks. We had shared our own success, a success that had led to an early retirement. A success that gave us a home in the winter sun of Tenerife and a home in the idyllic summer countryside of the garden of England that had followed the 14 memorable years in the Isle of Man which in turn had followed retirement at just 48 years old. We had shared so much that was good, the one thing we had never had to share, the one thing we had never had to deal with, was tragedy. And now, suddenly here was the potential for one of the biggest tragedies of them all, the realization that, a life of ease and enjoyment, a final twenty or so years where we would watch our children and grandchildren grow older and enjoy their own successes, was not ours by right. The realization that possibly, just possibly, we might not grow old together. These thoughts were unspoken whispers in the minds of us both. Time enough to put them into words.

We decided as one, on the charming restaurant in our own lovely village square, And, having made such an important decision, put the rest to the back of our minds whilst we prepared for an early bath.   Bath-time over, with our skin glowing, and our mixtures of Amani for men and Chanel No. 5 blending together, we toddled along the road and up the worn stone steps of The Lime Tree just as they were opening the doors.   We shoe-horned ourselves into our favourite window corner, and, as the sun began to set on the soldierly line of lime trees that surrounded the Square and from which the restaurant takes its name, I savoured my first Kir Royale of the day and taking our lead from the lime tree regiment outside the window, we mustered our thoughts into an orderly fashion. We talked about options.   We talked about hopes, We talked about family.   We talked about winters gone and winters to come.

As the sun sank lower over the square, as our melon and palma ham became our grilled salmon, as our grilled salmon became our crème brulee, as our crème brulee became our cheese and biscuits, as our cheese and biscuits became our café crème we watched the shadows lengthen.   In those shadows I knew the Tigers were gathering and that on this night not even the Kir Royales would keep them at bay.

A TIGER IS JUST A BIG PUSSY CAT WITH CLAWS

I am not even sure I slept that night.   Polly had said to me as we pulled the covers over us. "Don't forget, White Rabbits in the morning"

White Rabbits.   The silly words that simply HAD to be the first we uttered on the first day of every month.   Twelve times every year.   Almost FIVE HUNDRED times during our life together.   Those silly words, a spell, a token that brings you good luck for the whole of the month.   The words that ward off evil influences.   The words that ensure that nothing bad will happen to you or yours.   I MUST REMEMBER THEM IN THE MORNING

For a long time I just lay there.   I did not try to sleep, I did not invite the Tigers in.   I heard the clock chime twelve times.   "WHITE RABBITS, WHITE RABBITS, WHITE RABBITS, WHITE RABBITS".

Polly was lying quietly but I knew she was not asleep. I stroked her back.
Words did not seem appropriate.   I played a round of golf in my mind, each hole, each shot carefully analysed.   I must of dozed because the clock chimed one. One o'clock.   Then it struck FOUR times. It had not been one o'clock, the single chime had signified half past three, and now it was four o'clock. I closed my eyes tight against the Tigers, but it was too late......they were already there.

Fear...I hadn't seen for a while

The last time he had bounded into my mind, he had been 'all mouth and trousers' as my late Aunt Doris would have say. Loud, and sometimes illogical, and easily overcome by **Hope.** *He had been a shadow of the monster that now invaded my mind.. Then he had been a big pussy cat.*

Now, well now he was a Tiger, a ferocious beast with red glowing eyes, razor sharp claws and a roar that could swallow thunder.

"You really thought you were going to get away with it didn't you" he snarled. "I've been telling you all along. YOUV'E GOT CANCER, there's never a permanent way back from that. And now its in your bones, its in your pelvis, its in your abdomen. These people don't waste their time looking for things that aren't there. They said you MIGHT have prostate cancer AND YOU DID, now they've told you may have it in your bones. AND YOU WILL, OF COURSE YOU WILL, IT WILL BE ALL OVER THE PLACE BY NOW." Then he started linking things together that I had not thought of. He purred softly, but the words made sense. "Hasn't it occurred to you" he said "all this trouble with your foot?. The pain even after the operation that was supposed to cure it, that's the CANCER IN YOUR ANKLE BONES. And, what about when that golf buggy collapsed in Ireland a few weeks ago. You complained of a pain in your lower back for weeks. It hurt for a long time because THE CANCERS EVEN IN YOUR SPINE. And...you know

*how your fingers are always aching IT'S OBVIOUSLY
THE CANCER,   And what about...................*

*And   what   about...................And   what
about.................And what about....................."*

*My Tiger, **Fear,** spent the night analysing every
pain I'd ever had.   Of course, it all made sense
now.   If you've got CANCER IN YOUR BONES,
you will have pains.   Long before the night was
over I had reached a numbing acceptance of the
worst news in the world.   My other Tigers visited,
but they were half-hearted in their feeble roars.
They knew there was not much point.*

Hope said
*Wait and see what the lovely Nita says....its
probably just a precaution.*

*But there was no conviction in **Hope's** words.*

Resignation said
*If it's in your bones, it's in your bones you'll
probably have a bit of a fight on your hands, but
you can't do a thing about it.*

Regret said
*Going private back in June might have helped,
you could have got it all out of the way quicker.
Still its probably been in your bones a long time
and the odd week here or there has probably made
no difference.*

Strangely enough it was Hope who had the last word.

It probably is only a precaution.....just wait and see what the lovely Nita says tomorrow.   You'll be fine.   I promise you....You'll be fine.

CHAPTER 13
'A POLICEMAN'S LOT IS
NOT A HAPPY ONE'

SEPTEMBER 2004

Despite spending most of the night awake, I had no difficulty getting up at sparrow fidget. I made Polly a cup of tea and took it back into the bedroom. It was not quite a first, but it was a little unusual. Now, it has to be said that I am the least chauvinistic chap you will ever meet.

Misogyny and me seldom, no, never, travel on the same bus. *Positively Uxorious* as my very good friend Billy used to tell me as month after month I fought the Lady's corner at the Golf Club committee meetings.

Now, if you want *'Misogyny'* that's where you could get it by the bucketful. However, non-misogynist that I am, it has to be said that I do have an old fashioned, and not necessarily to be admired, traditional male trait. I am the laziest domestic partner in the world. Talk about 'Can't cook, won't cook,' with me you can add the whole range. 'Can't hoover, won't hoover,' Can't dust won't dust,' Can't iron won't iron,' well you get the picture. But, before you brand me a couch potato hear my defence. I have been spoiled rotten by the love of two very special women, having been both an *'only child'* and an *'only husband'.* I have never lived alone.

I lived with my mother for my first 22 years, and with my wife for the following 40. I have never been big on household chores because I have always been waited on hand and both feet.

Frankly, I blame the police. Let me explain.

I was married in March 1965, the good 'ole days' when a future Bridegroom's *'stag'* night was a *'stagger'* around a dozen pubs or so in or around the vicinity of the church that was booked for the following days nuptials. By convention the stag night invariable preceded a *'thick head',* which was often followed by a *'thick ear'* once the *'spinster of this parish'* had successfully changed her status. Of course today's bridegroom tends to prefer a *'stag fortnight'* around the girlie bars of Amsterdam.

And who's to say they are wrong. Times change but Ces't la Vie, or as they say in France. *'Nous wouldn't have wanted it anyway......would nous?'*

Let's leave the question rhetorical and continue with my rather conventional 'stag night of good intent'.

A dozen or so close acquaintances took me out to the aforementioned dozen or so pubs, where I probably had a dozen or so glasses of mild and bitter. At that time the only Kir I had heard of was Kier Hardy, and in any event I was far to young for Kir Royales, to say nothing of Amsterdam Girlie Bars. When the pubs were closed we repaired (and, I seem to remember that some of us needed repairing) back to the offices of one Billy Brindle (of whom less later).

Billy was a friend, but also happened to be my boss - destined some years later to become my partner (short-term). His office was over the old National Provincial Bank in Margate. It was three o'clock in the morning, as I am sure Frank Sinatra was reminding us through the medium of a scratchy circle of vinyl played upon a cute little piece of machinery called *'a record player'* . This was, of course, in those long ago days before he started singing in Chinese Medicinal Centres. A combination of the lateness (or extreme earliness) of the hour and the noise emanating from those well lit premises attracted the attention of a large man dressed entirely in blue, who used to walk up and down the deep night roads shining his torch into dark corners. He must have assumed that here, in a room above the banking hall of the Nat Pro. were a ruthless gang of ne'er-do-wells planning to tunnel through, the ceiling above to the banking hall below, so that they could be the first in the queue to cash a cheque when the bank opened. Never mind, whatever his thought processes, they led to him bravely ringing the bell of the glazed door which led to the first floor, and through which his helmeted and be-truncheoned form could clearly be seen. One of the lads had half walked, half fallen down the single flight of stairs to let him, in singing in a loud voice 'A pleeceman's lot is not a 'nappy one' "Allo Allo Allo" our policeman might have said, but didn't "What's going on 'ere then?" he might have continued, as he walked up the stairs, and did.

"My very good friend Basil is getting married tomorrow and we are wetting the babies head" said Billy Brindle, "You must come in ossifer and hab a drink with my ex-friend" added Billy's brother Tony who was pretty much pissed off, on account of the fact that, as my oldest friend, he had expected to be my best man - and wasn't.

"Not while I'm on duty sir" the ossifer might have said, but didn't "Just a small one, as it's a special occasion sir" he might have said, and did. And, as he lifted his glass, this bastion of the beat, this pride of the peelers, this hardened hand of the law said "alright then", he looked around the room, "ooze the groom?"

"Ooze the groom?" several of us echoed, wondering if it could be some form of 'on the spot' punishment for making a noise over the Nat Pro.

We stared at him blankly. "Ooze the groom?" he repeated looking from one face to another with a purposeful stare. The penny dropped slowly, settling gently into the collective gallons of mild and bitter.

"Basil here" said a sudden chorus of voices pushing me forward

"Well Basil, young man, I've been married 35 years" wow, 35 years, a lifetime to someone who was still under 22 years old, "I am going to give you a piece of advice which is simple, but will get you out of many a scrape, and ensure you have a calm and untroubled married life." A dozen or so young men stood quietly glasses half way to their lips. This was after all going to be pearls of wisdom from a man who was not only the best of the boys in blue, but older than Methusala himself. How else can you have been married for 35 years. When the advice came, none of us were disappointed. He rocked backwards and forwards on his heels, He placed his hands on his hips. He leaned forward until his ancient old face was just a few inches from my own youthful visage.

"IF YOU MAKE THE TEA EVERY DAY IT'S EXPECTED. BUT IF YOU MAKE IT NOW AND AGAIN IT'S APPRECIATED."

I've never forgotten his words, and today............. I made the Tea.

This morning was to be my first visit to the splendid new surgery which had housed my doctors group practice for just a few days. It was ten minutes to eight and I was amazed to find the fairly small car-park already almost overflowing. I found a space and sat there waiting for the big hand to point to the sky. After about five minutes another car pulled into the car park and took the one remaining space next to me. A young lady got out, looked at me, and, with her head on one side, enquiringly, smiled. I opened my window and smiled back.

"The surgery does open at 8 o'clock doesn't it?", I asked.

"It does" she said but why are you parked in the staff car park.

"Whoops," I said, "where should I go?" She pointed the way, and five minutes later I was the first into the lobby, as the receptionist, having opened the front door, prepared for another day at the ranch.

"I would like an appointment with Dr Hakelin," I smiled

"She's at Harrietsham today," my smile was returned

"Can I still make an appointment, it is rather urgent?"

"I'm sorry, but you will have to go to Harrietsham and make it there, we're not supposed to use the computer for appointments other than at this surgery."

"The computer will do it then?"

"Not on its own," she smiled, but if we ask it, it can do almost anything BUT, appointments, other than here, only in an emergency." What a long answer I thought, but *'talk the talk'* and you are half-way there. It was here that I put my *'worst foot'* forward and my silver topped cane to best theatrical effect.

"I see, I said, I'm sorry to have troubled you" Grunting in supposed pain, I turned, and leaning heavily on my stick and took a few shuffly steps towards the door, then I turned back, with my very best grimace as I felt the pain shoot up my walking stick.

"Sorry to trouble you again," I smiled the smile I'd picked up from *'the lovely Nita'* - except that I used my own teeth. " but how do I get to Har.. riet...sham." I stumbled over the word, the carpet and the nearest plastic chair. I saw a frown of sympathy begin to crease her forehead.

"What is your name?" she asked in her best *'I'm going to help you'* voice.

"Jay," I said "Basil Jay" I could hear the James Bond theme playing in my mind. She glanced at my knuckles, white from the unnecessary pressure I was exerting upon my silver topped cane.

"Well Mr Jay....perhaps this is an emergency after all, when would you like to see Dr Hakelin?". She smiled....I beamed.

"As soon as possible please." She fumbled with her computer.

"Is 9.30 this morning OK?"

"9.30 this morning is just perfect. *tu erres muy amable* ,You are very kind" I said

"De Nada," don't mention it, she replied smiling. OK so everybody goes to Spain for their holidays.

"Thank you" I mouthed, and made my way to the door still remembering to lean, just a little

96

more than was necessary, upon my silver topped cane.

It was not until I was back in the car park that realized that I hadn't asked her how to get to Harrietsham, and although I knew damn well, she didn't know that *'Eso la Vida'*.... or as the Spanish say - 'That's life'

Basil Jay please go to room 2. I was very impressed by the silently moving sign that indicates when it's your turn in a modern Doctors surgery.

Perhaps I nostalgically remembered the old "NEXT PLEASE" called out by the departing patient of yesteryear. It was 9.30 exactly, the system was working perfectly.

"Hello Basil, How are you?"

"Well, daily struggling with the fact that I feel so well so how can I be so ill" Nita smiled

"Funny things prostates" she whispered.

"Yes", I said, thinking that anything that is walnut sized and prune shaped has got to be on a hiding to nothing.

"How did you get on at the results clinic?" she said

"That's why I've come to see you," I said, "You see, everything's gone .... prune shaped".

"Oh", she raised her eyebrows "How so?"

"They want me to have a bone scan and an MRI scan"

"Oh they always do that, just a precaution" she genuinely did not seem the least bit worried.

"The Doctor said that at the multi-discipline meeting they were not convinced that my cancer had not spread ". She pretended to tear her hair out.

"These surgeons, they make me so angry, they have absolutely no people skills at all, I bet he just came straight out with it, didn't explain why......no people skills at all" she repeated, "that's why they're surgeons"

I was beginning to feel better.

"So you don't think I need worry too much?"

"I don't think you should worry at all, I've already told you IT'S TITCHY."

I was beginning to feel MUCH better.

"How long,?" I asked, "do you think I will have to wait for the scans."

"Well, the bone scan should not be too bad, but the MRI, well, even URGENT cases are waiting up to three months"

"I'd like to go Private I said, what do I have to do?" She steepled her fingers

"Well, it will be expensive" she said

"Life is more important than money," I said glibly, thinking of the £3,500 for my A.R.F...... and assuming a similar amount. I better make sure I thought. "How much are we talking?" I said, "about £5,000" adding a bit to the cost of a foot, by allowing for its comparative inaccessibility. .

"Probably double that" she said, "it's a shame you're not insured" Just at that moment an interesting thought hit me, perhaps, just perhaps

I was insured. Something for me to look into later. She went on.

"I will send a letter of referral today to Mr Breading, if you telephone the department of nuclear science and arrange the scans, tell them you are private and tell them that Mr Breading has the referral letter."

"How long do think?" I said

"Well she said, Winterlands do MRI scans on Sundays, and Alexandra on Wednesdays.   You will certainly be seen at one of them within the week.

"What a difference" I said.   Nita just smiled.

I thanked her, and left the surgery.   The drive back home was only about 5 miles, but there was such a spring in my step again that I could have done it faster on foot than in the car   I couldn't wait to get home and do some telephoning.

And the Tigers - they could hunt elsewhere tonight.

CHAPTER 14
A MODERN FACE

SEPTEMBER 2004

Here I was walking alone through the brand-new wing of the Oncology Department and the Department of Nuclear Science.

It was *'state of the art'*. A modern interior all lying beneath an architects best dream. A flowing canopy of white plastic, designed to look like a tent. I am not denigrating it, it looked splendidly modern and dispelled for ever the institutional gloom of so many hospitals still housed as they are, in either frightful Victorian edifices that look for all the world like a Dickensian work-house, or the hideous, flat roof, Ferrous concrete monstrosities that grew out of the brave new world (architecturally speaking) of the late fifties and sixties.

I walked past rows of ergonomically designed chairs, that were, I hoped and believed, far more comfortable than they looked.   I sidled around monstrous ferns made of real leaves and stalks, and past delightful and GENUINE potted palm trees and Swiss cheese plants.   I glanced at the modernistic prints upon the wall, and the huge airy windows that looked over an enclosed courtyard patio with tables and chairs set out in the style of a Paris café.   There was so much to see.   The only thing I could not see were.........people.   At 6 o'clock at night, this was a ghost hospital.

The reception counters were abandoned.   The small, but very smart coffee bar in this space-age lobby was silent, towels were draped across the coffee machine.   There were not even cleaners in evidence.   It was 6 o'clock in the evening, and I was about fifteen minutes late for my appointment. It seemed that everyone had gone home.

Had a *'rough prostrate warning'* been given out over the tannoy by the nurse of the white plastic cup?

"Basil Jay approaches, begone, begone".

Had the car park attendant who assisted at my spleen removal yelled out a *'Troublesome spleen warning?'*.

"Protect your cars, troublesome spleen approaching".

A young lady in a white coat walked towards me.

"Mr Jay" she said

"Yes" I said, "I'm sorry I'm late I didn't allow for the heavy tea-time traffic" she waved away my apology.

"That's OK" she said "You're here now, that's all that matters"

"Where is everyone?" I asked sweeping my arm around the empty spaces.

"We close at 5.30" she said "I said I'd be happy to hang on for you"

I was strangely relieved to find I wasn't *'persona non grata'*

"That's very kind of you" I said...... because it was.   THIS, I thought, is the NHS that everybody complains about.   Then I remembered the day of the White Plastic Cup.

I reflected back.   After seeing the lovely Nita, exactly one week before, I had raced home and picked up the telephone.

"The department of Nuclear Science, please" I said to the girl on the switchboard

"Just putting you through" said the voice

"Nuclear" said a new voice "Joan speaking, can I help?"

"Oh hello.....Joan" I said, "my name is Basil Jay"

"Basil" she said in a wagging her finger sort of voice

"You should have been here at 9.30"

"Why, what happened?" I wanted to say, but didn't "I beg your pardon" I said questioningly.

"Your appointment for a bone scan was for 9.30 on the 1ˢᵗ - we rushed it through", she said

"I'm sorry", I said, "I didn't know"

"We wrote to you on the 28ᵗʰ, Mr Breading wanted us to see you quickly"

"I've had no letter" I replied, "but I'm so grateful for your promptness. And so sorry I've missed the appointment"

"Never mind she said, lets see what we can do" There was silence for a few seconds. "Can you come on Tuesday at about a quarter to six?" she asked. "We already have you booked in for an MRI scan on Thursday the 9ᵗʰ". That's an omen I thought, September 9ᵗʰ is my youngest sons birthday. "at 1.45", she continued.

"Absolutely, I said and thank you once again for being so helpful" then I added, "I only told my GP I wanted to go private about two hours ago, and she said I should get appointments within the week, but this is remarkable - when did you get the note?".

"This isn't a private appointment" said Joan, "I have you down as a NHS patient"   I explained my reasons for wanting to change.

"Scans are expensive she said, why don't you have them on the NHS as you're all booked in, and then change to private for your consultants appointment and whatever treatment he recommends. That will speed things up."

"Thank you Joan", I whispered, "You have all been so very kind"

And thus it was in an empty Oncology and Nuclear Science department, that a young lady in a white coat showed further dedication to an NHS patient by staying late so that I could have my scan.

"Let's start, shall we?" said lady white coat "Have you ever had a body scan before?" she smiled and I immediately felt at ease.

"No" I said, "Never"

"Well" she said "Your part is fairly easy, although a bit boring, all you have to do is lie very still for about twenty to thirty minutes. The only things you have to take off is your glasses as the scanner passes quite close to your face. If you will feel more comfortable with your shoes off, you can take those off as well" She smiled again "Any questions?"

"No, I don't think so," I smiled back.

"Well lets get started" she led me to a long couch affair which appeared to be on rails. The couch was in the middle of the room and I was relieved to see that there was no wall to face. Over the couch a large semi-circular barrel was suspended on overhead supports. Between the supports was a mobile of brightly coloured ducks cut out of cardboard and suspended on cotton. Oh the cleverness of technology.

"Now what will happen is this," she said, "you will lie here on the couch and very very slowly the couch will move along the rails and through the tube. It will start at your feet, and, as I said, will take between twenty and thirty minutes to complete the journey.   Once the tube is over your face you may feel a bit claustrophobic because it comes very close , that's why it's best to take off your glasses.   Just try to lie still.   When the scanner has finished its traverse I will take some extra scans of your upper body region where the tube doesn't quite get a clear picture....any questions?"

"Its very kind of you to work late like this, I do appreciate it."

"Oh I don't mind at all, sorting you out is more important than me having an early tea" I smiled my gratitude, it was turning out to be a smiley sort of occasion.

"Right...very still now" and that was it, I lay there very still and the tube passed over me as the couch rolled along the runners.   It occurred to me how highly unusual it was in these violent, employer aware days, that an attractive young lady should allow herself, and *be* allowed to be alone with a man in a large and empty building. I didn't raise it, she probably wouldn't want to be reminded anyway.   Soon it was over. I wished lady white coat goodbye and thanked her once more for missing her tea. Then I walked out of the still deserted building and to my car in the now deserted car park.

I could not help but ask the question.   "is really this the NHS that everybody ridicules and Criticises?"

Two days later I was back.   It was the same, but it was so very different.   Reception was buzzing, four girls dealing with lines of people. A board behind reception indicated that in addition to the Body Scan and MRI Scanning departments, no less that five consultants were currently holding court. A white board behind the girls heads was constantly being updated to show waiting times. Across the way the coffee bar, which, it must be said would have graced any airport lounge, was doing a roaring trade. No man with a badge and a white plastic cup here. Oh bless you no. Did I hanker for the good 'ole days' of a month ago?.... no I did not.

"Hello", I said to a smiling face "Mr Jay, I have an MRI scan at 1.45"

"Hello Mr Jay, MRI have their own reception. Just follow the signs, I am sure they will be ready for you" I followed the signs to reception, they were ready for me.   As I reached the counter I was met by a bright and cheerful smile.

"Mr Jay?" the smile said

"It is" I said, quite amazed

"Just sit over there and Joan will come and see you"

My nether cheeks had hardly moulded into the comfortable shape of the ergonomic masterpiece called 'chair', when, "Hello Mr Jay, I'm Joan" I looked up. Hang on, can this be the same hospital as the dignity stripping 'white plastic cup,' of the insensitive 'I spoke to Napoleon' reading matter, of the gowns tailored for midgets.

"Hello Joan, thank you very much for arranging everything so quickly"

"You're very welcome, now come along and get changed, we just have a bit of paper work, and then we can get you sorted out."

I followed into a small ante-room with a large disabled toilet off, and two or three lockers with keys along the wall.

"If you would like to go inside and take your clothes off.   You will find pyjama trousers and jackets behind the door.   There should be some to fit you.   Then just put your things into a locker. The doctor will take the key when you go in for your scan. I will be watching for you and come and see you as soon as you're ready."

The pyjamas fitted.   I locked my clothes away and was no sooner seated when Joan was back. "Right, Basil, just a few questions" I nodded "Have you removed ALL of your jewellery?"

"Yes I have"

"Have you any metal in your body, pins, plates, staples etc.?"

"No", I said, not now, I explained about my ankle. I do have some dental implants" I said. She looked at her form, that will be OK, she said, we are just concentrating on the Pelvic and Abdominal regions, so we shouldn't have you spinning around and around on the table".

"What is an MRI scan?", I asked, quite surprised that I had let so much time elapse without asking the question.

"MRI stands for Magnetic Resonance Imaging" said Joan "and magnets and metal have an infinity which could be unfortunate in an unguarded moment"

"Ah" I said, knowingly

"Shall we go through" The doctor was young and friendly

"Hello Mr Jay, have you ever had an MRI scan before?"

"No, I haven't, but Joan has just explained what it is" I said

"Good.....good" He turned towards the large machine that did seem to be a complete, solid sided cage. "Now, one or two things you should know. It's a bit tight in there, and once you are in-side won't be able to hear you. Now what I am going to do is give you this lead which has a bulb on the end. If you want a rest, and want to come out just press the bulb once. I want you to put these headphones on, there a three reasons for this. First, it will cut out the noise of the machine. Second, I can play you some music - anything you like. Did you bring a CD with you?"

"No, I didn't"

"Not to worry, what kind of music do you like?"

"Something restful - Rachmaninov perhaps"

"Can't do that, but I can give you classic FM, you never know, it might be 'lunch time with Rachmaninov.' " He smiled, I smiled back. "Thirdly", he was back to business, "I can talk to you and tell you what I'm doing."

"Any questions?"

"No thank you, I don't think so."

"OK, lets roll. Jump up, lie on your back and get comfortable...whoops, we'll have to have the glasses off, the top of the tube is only a fraction away from your face."

"Here you are" I said, handing him my glasses, and then, remembering, my locker key handed that over as well.

"Relax.........Ready?"

"②✍✍①③❸☎⓪✍☎▯⓪③&☎③▯▮ ☎③✐" I thought

"Wedddy" I said. Making sure I was fully Weelaxed.

Chopin's Nocturn in Eb came through the headphones "Nice" I thought.   Nice, but short lived.

"OK Mr Jay, I going to talk to you now, you don't have to answer, but I want to tell you what I plan to do" even though I didn't have to answer, I felt myself nod.   "First I am going to give you a little test burst lasting just 1 minute.   It will be very noisy but that is normal.   After that you will have two busts of 4 minutes each and then three consecutive, each of about 6 minutes duration. Between each burst I will give you a minutes rest. Now you will feel nothing, the noise is normal, but if you want to come up for air just press the bulb in hand"   I nodded again

"Right, off we go."   Chopin came back but soon lost his battle with the noise of the MRI scanner. After each burst the doctor would quietly say "OK, just rest a minute" I would rest

"Now a four minute burst" Eventually it was over.   It was painless. For me, it was not that unpleasant, although I would feel for anyone with a fear of confined spaces.   I got dressed.   On the way out Joan said, "I will make sure the scans all get to Mr Breading, just give us a few days. If you phone Mr Breading's secretary, she is at Winterlands, she should be able book you in for his next clinic which is next Friday the 17th.   Good luck."

"Thank you Joan,....for everything" I walked back through the bustle of the main reception. Everything so modern.   Smart receptionists in stylish skirts and blouses and smiles (it was most certainly a smiley sort of place) upon their faces. It is amazing how a new and modern building can change so much.   Could this be the NHS of the future.

When I got home I telephoned Mr Breading's secretary.   Yes, she had my referral letter, yes Mr Breading would be delighted to have me as a private patient.   Yes, an appointment at his next clinic was fine.   "Shall we say 10.30 on the 17th Mr Jay, or would 2.45 suit you better?"

"10.30 will be fine" I said, "thank you."

"10.30 it is, then, and I will make sure Mr Breading has had a chance to study your scan results.

The realization that I had had the scans and somebody, somewhere would soon know my destiny hit me on the way home and much of the comfort given me by the lovely Nita evaporated. Just a week to go, and we will know.   Still too early to make plans. Never to early to have hopes. And a little project to take my mind off things. Tomorrow I will investigate the insurance situation. Until then, however, I have dinner for two to look forward to this evening, and tonight.......

The Tigers who, sure as big oaks from little acorns grow, will come tonight.

CHAPTER 15
ALL THIS FOR A
DOLLAR A WEEK

SEPTEMBER 2004

One of the most memorable lines from the original film of *'The Producers'*, with Mel Brooks and Gene Wilder, occurred when the Gene Wilder character was being sold an insurance policy. Inevitably the salesman was expansive in his description of the benefits accruing to the policy. Having heard him out Gene Wilder says in an awed voice. *'You mean to say I get all this for just a dollar a week'* (stay with me, there is a point)

In my first life, I was a surveyor by qualification, a property *dealer* by inclination, and a property *developer* by aspiration. I refer to 'my first life' because it was kind to me and enabled me to retire when I was just 48 years old. When my partner and I sold our company in 1990, we did pretty well, the sale created for us both - a comfortable sum.   On the day we completed the sale, my solicitor and long-time friend asked me *"Have you now got a pile big enough to hide behind?"*   Well the short answer was, no, not quite. The problem was, retiring at 48, with, God willing, a hopeful expectation of 30 years or more in retirement, the pile has to be rather higher than it would if retiring at 68.   Twenty more years to fill the bucket, twenty less years to empty it.

No!, the pile was not high enough. I suspect that even crouched down low, my head and half my torso would still be visible above the parapet. However, fate was to take a hand, and a modest pile was made a little higher following a chance meeting with a man who knew a man who once danced with the sister of a man who lived on the Isle of Man.

Following a convoluted procedure I met, some weeks later, in the Institute of Directors in London's Pall Mall, a man who we will call simply, Reg - on account of that being his name.

Simply Reg, who some years earlier had himself become a tax exile from Southern Island, led me by the hand - or was it the nose, through the intricacies of Offshore companies, Offshore Trusts, and legal cash in brown envelopes.   The essence was easy to grasp.   An offshore trust has certain tax exemptions, whilst an offshore company owes its tax only to the jurisdiction of it's incorporation at the tax rate set by that jurisdiction.   The rate was often a single duty of, seldom more than

£250 irrespective of the assets and wealth of the company. Capital Gains Tax (my main immediate concern) and Inheritance Tax (a distant possible commitment) were not a part of the offshore world's vocabulary.

Of course, avoiding Capital Gains Tax on the sale of the company and other personal assets, increased the size of the aforementioned modest pile by a further 40% (in round figures). This totally legitimate opportunity simply required me to leave (or so I thought at the time) the UK and become an overseas resident for three years. Simply Reg (for such he had become known) was a gem or perhaps I became his gem as he realized that, knowing nothing, I trusted him totally in my naivety. As this process had started long before my partner, whom I shall call Ken, on account of that being *his* name, finally completed the sale of our Company.

Consequently we still shared our large comfortable office with desks at respective ends and comfortable couches and coffee table in the centre. The phone would ring. Ken, being far more athletic than I, would have the instrument to his ear before my hand had left the desk. What a gunfighter he would have made. "Yes, he's here", I would hear him say.

"It's *'Simply Reg'* for you" he would call switching the phone onto loudspeaker.

"Good Morning Reg" I would say - dropping the Simply.

"Basil, how are you?" pause " I've been thinking about your problem."

He always started his conversations this way. "Another £2000 down the drain" Ken would mouth across the wide divide. I would glare him into silence.

"I think you should perhaps wrap everything up in a Nevis company" Reg would say.

"But Reg" I would answer, I already have a Southern Ireland Company, a UK Company, A BVI Company, a Jersey Trust, a Guernsey Company and a pain in the wallet. And where the hell is Nevis anyway?"

"Oh out there with all the others - did you know?" he would continue before I could get too geographically probing, "there are over 200 Tax Havens throughout the world - and one of them is called the Kingdom of Melkizadek?".

"And you want me to have a company in each of them?" I answered tightly.

"Not at all" said Simply Reg, obviously realising he had just about had the last feather from the Golden Goose. "This one will really wrap it up".

"How much Reg?" I said with the tone of resignation he had gratefully come to recognise.

"£2000" we said together with Ken joining in with a chortle from across the room.

"How would you like it?" I would ask

"Can you do cash?" we all answered together with Ken joining in from a prone position on the floor in front of his desk whilst banging his fists on the floor in absolute glee.

"Where,?" I would ask following the script.

"Can we meet at the Institute of Directors in Pall Mall?" we answered together with Ken now laying on his back, kicking his legs and pumping his arms in the air with delight, as he broke into his usual parody of 'The Irish Rover'

"2000 for Ireland, just 2000 more,
2000 for Jersey will level the score,
2000 for Nevis, and Guernsey too hoooooo,
2000 for Reg and he blesses you...........
2000 for..............."

"Belt up Ken", I yelled cutting off the words but leaving the laughter rebounding off the office walls.

I was not so green as I was cabbage looking, and, although I realized I was 'paying through the nose', (there was to become a time, it must be said, when Ken thought I had got away very cheaply, and, although I would love to give you chapter and verse now, it must, as they say, remain a story for another day).

I had been carrying out much research into the intricacies of Offshore Trusts, Nominee Companies, and Beneficial Ownerships. *(stick with me OK, its relevant - its all about private medical insurance)* Polly was brilliant. When I said we needed to make a life changing move, to leave friends of more than twenty years and go and live on a rain battered rock, she did not bat an outward eye. *What her inward eyes were doing I have no idea.*

And so.....we sold up our family home.   We had an auction on the premises of our 22 room country house, and sold all but a few treasured possessions. We moved to the Isle of Man, that windy and wet, but oh so beautiful rock in the middle Irish Sea. We went alone because my eldest son had his own home in Eastbourne, My daughter had set off to live as an Au Pair in Paris, and my youngest son was bound for University.

We loved the island.   We met many so-called *'Tax Exiles'* almost on our arrival.   1990 was obviously a good year for leaving the UK or Southern Ireland.   Of our first three acquaintances, who became close friends, there was Billy a little Irishman from Dublin who had made a fortune out of photocopiers and was known for his sharp wit and personal catchphrase *'I'm a happy little scamp'*.

There was Wayne, tall and suave, who had feathered his nest from employment agencies. And there was Ken.   Gruffly pleasant, who had made a killing in windscreen wipers.   Most people did their three years tax penance (some called it their Inland Revenue induced prison sentence), quite legitimately avoided capital gains tax on the sale of their businesses and assets, and then returned to the UK, or in many cases Southern Ireland, to make a new fortune.   So it was with both Wayne and Ken. But not me, and not Billy   I took to the island with a passion, both Polly and I did, a passion so great that we lived a very contented life there for almost fourteen years.   We both became Captains of the premier golf club on the island, and often found ourselves at dinner parties with island government ministers and the commercial and church heirachy.

The Isle of Man is a microcosm of the UK.   It has its own parliament - the oldest in the world - and its own laws and fiscal policies.   For the first two years I did everything I thought I would want to do when I retired.   I played golf every day, and my handicap came down from 20 to 11.   I wrote the book that everyone is said to have inside of them.   I even wrote a musical on the life of Nelson. But, it has to be said, I missed the cut and thrust of commercial life.   So. In 1992, I bought the controlling interest in a firm, of Corporate Service Providers.   Company management specialists, exactly the sort of thing that 'Simply Reg' did, creating offshore tax efficient structures for the *aspiring* (and sometimes even *expiring)* and tax-avoiding rich   In other words I Became 'Simply Basil,' with, I have to say, the same desire to help as did 'Simply Reg,' but with not quite the same propensity to 'help myself' as he did.   I wanted no-one rolling around the floor singing any version of 'The Irish Rover' on my account.

Thus began my second life *(it is relevant, I promises.....just hold the word INSURANCE in your mind).*   Within a year I had acquired 100% of the shareholding, and, with just two staff looked forward to a gentle dabble in the world of offshore.

By 1998, I had around 300 clients and 15 staff.   I was working harder in my second life, that I had in my first.   I was flying from the island to the UK at least once a week and 'stopping over' - and horror of horrors, my handicap had crept back up from 11 to 18.   *'That's life,'* or, as Esther Rantzen used to say.......*'That's life'*

By 1998 I had had enough, I kept about 20 clients who had become friends, I kept the company, and 'sold' on very extended credit, the clients data base to the staff.   I then looked forward to the gentle dabble I had hoped for in 1992.   There was now, just me, Polly, and an attic office in our cliff-top home overlooking the beautiful harbour of Port St Mary.

By late 1999, my 20 clients had become 50 (friends of friends etc.) and I was chasing my tail again.   I knew well, through another business interest I had, a young lady who, next to a huge heart had had a dynamo installed.   It was clear to us both that the business we were both involved in (me as simply a non-executive director) did not offer her the scope that she and her untiring energy deserved.   To simplify the story, I asked Sharron to join me as my PA.   Within a year she had trebled the business.   Within 18 months I had given her, gladly, 50% of the business she had had such a dynamic affect upon... Four years later, she has offices in four countries and getting on for 40 staff.   I am life chairman of the company I founded, but now have the happiest of retirements, going to board meetings once a month (if I am in the country) and generally interfering.   OK so what's this got to do with prostates as big as plums.   What is the word I told you to hold in your mind...........*INSURANCE*   Right, listen to this.

I recalled, that in May, Sharron had telephoned me to say she was thinking of taking out a corporate health policy to provide private medicine for members of staff within the group. What did I think?.   Well, Sharron and I have many things in common, not the least of which is our shared believe that the most important asset of a company are the people who work for it.   I agreed, without reservation.   I next recalled that in an unconnected conversation she had told me she had completed the insurance, it commenced immediately, "oh, and by the way, I have included you in the policy....you are the Company Chairman, after all" I had no knowledge of the terms of the policy or if it included pathetic prostates. But, there was certainly no harm in finding out.   I asked the girls to send me a copy of the policy. They did, and, on the face of it, it appeared a possibility that I might be covered.   Despite the small print, the company she had chosen was first class.   I will not embarrass them by naming them. As you will now gather, after a few investigative enquiries, they confirmed that I was indeed covered for anything that the medical profession chose to throw at me - providing I had not had it before, I had not even thought of getting it, I had never stood next to anyone in a bus who might have had it, and I had not read any books where it was mentioned.

And so, with that comfortable knowledge firmly in my head, I girded my loins, as you do, and waited the coming of the 17th September. My second results clinic, and the one at which, with the results of all my scans in place, I would learn exactly what my future held.

CHAPTER 16
BASIL, YOU'RE ONE
IN A HUNDRED

SEPTEMBER/OCTOBER 2004

The Tigers hadn't worried me for some time.

It's a very strange thing, but the human mind has a level of acceptance which is quite remarkable. Of course, there are times of intense fear when facing the unknown.

There are moments of incredible anger that you...YOU...should be put in a position of danger.

There are moments of huge sadness, partly a great sadness at what, selfishly, you will miss. The family you will not see develop through their lives. The successes they enjoy, that you will not be a part of. The golf you will no longer play. The holidays you will no longer enjoy. The sumptuous fare. The fine champagnes. The great companionship of dinner parties with friends, of which you have had your last. The love, and the romantic interludes (a euphemism) that you would have enjoyed until the moment of rigor mortis (and possibly beyond).   That is the selfish sadness. That is the *'poor me'* syndrome.   *I* am being short-changed.   *I* am not getting my three score years and ten ...... plus a bit.   *I* am the victim.   WHY ME?.   Then you get to think...WHY NOT ME?.   I am out of it, I leave behind me the real sadness.   The inflicted sadness.   The sadness that will invade the lives of those you love, and from whom you are prematurely parted..........for ever.   The long sleepless nights your mother will spend.   The long and lonely days and nights and possibly years your wife will spend.   The voice that will no longer be on the end of the 'phone for a son or a daughter wanting to share a success or a failure, a moment of joy or a time of despair.   The grandson who will always be missing one grandfather, and whose life, one arrogantly supposes, will be a little less full in that missing.   The lessons your children and your grandchildren will no longer learn based on your own experiences.   The intense pain of these realizations gradually lessens to a strange acceptance.   *'Isn't it a shame that'?* or ' *I will be missing so much*' and then you realize, that what will really happen is so simple.   You will go to sleep, and you won't wake up.   There will be no pain, your pain will have come whilst you are living, the pain for those who are left will come after you have gone.   Those bloody Tigers. Today, we will know.

I had no difficulty leaping out of bed at seven o'clock.   I made Polly a cup of tea (if I am not too

123

careful, the pleasant *appreciated* will become the dreaded *accepted)*. I took a coffee into the conservatory, watched the autumn leaves fall from the majestic horse chestnuts that abound our garden, and waited for the big hand to tell me that we could set off to confront Mr Breading, and learn the best .... or the worst. We gave ourselves 40 minutes to do a 15 minute journey, and, sod's law, we needed every minute. We pulled into the hospital car park at 10.25. I introduced myself at reception, and the receptionist said. "Good Morning Mr Jay, please take a seat and Mr Breading will be with you shortly". I looked around reception and the waiting room, and remembered the day of the white plastic cup. Chalk and cheese. Chalk and bloody cheese. The décor was quietly refined. Attractive plants adorned each corner. The current days newspapers for all tastes, were on strategically place coffee tables, soft music played in the background. My lower cheeks had hardly created a niche in the softly upholstered chair before a nurse came up to me. "Mr Jay", she said, "Mr Breading is ready for you now" She looked at Polly. "Mrs Jay?" she enquired, Polly smiled and nodded , "would you like to come through as well?". This was the first time Polly had accompanied me. It wasn't for lack of trying on her part, but each time I had insisted that I would be fine on my own. Probably some sort of man-thing. This morning she had said

"I'm coming into the consultants with you". This morning, I had not argued. *Private* Mr

Breading was standing behind his desk, but walked around it to shake our hands, and introduce himself to Polly.   *NHS* Mr Breading, had stayed seated with eyes riveted on his notes until I was seated and nervous. Mark you, if I had to deal with the nurse of the white plastic cup on a regular basis, I would have lost *my* grasp on the niceties of life.

"Good morning Mr Jay," he said,

"Good morning" I responded, "This is my wife," I grinned, "I'm here to listen to what you say, and Anne" (posh name for Polly) "has come along to remember it."   He smiled

"Mrs Jay,"   he said, please sit down"

My bones were lying all over his desk, my abdominal and pelvic region were curling up at the edges. He picked me up by my tibia, or it might have been my fibia and held me to the light. He barely glanced at the plate and then directed his gaze at me.

"Your bone scan is quite clear" he said, in much the same tone he might have used to ask if I took milk in my coffee.   "Your MRI was perfectly OK as well."   Now, I pride myself on being as bright as the next man, always providing the next man isn't a budding Einstein.   "Do you mean that my cancer hasn't spread?" I said.

"Your cancer appears to be confined to the prostate itself" he said.

"Yesssssss" I thought, mentally punching the air with my fist.

"BUT".   he said

"BUT, BUT, BUT", I thought, there is always a bloody BUT.

"The tests do not show the lymph nodes, IF, we operate, then we will take a biopsy, it is only then that we can be sure"

"*If* you operate?". I said,

"My recommendation" he said but I would like to take you through the options". I sat back and waited.

"You can have *Hormonal Therapy*, this takes the form of a *Luteinizing Hormone-Releasing Hormone.* You can have an *Orchietomy*" He sort of smiled. "for all practical purposes that is castration"

"Ouch", I thought, I said nothing, just gave an appropriate grimace, whilst waiting for Polly to put her hand up, bounce up and down in her seat shouting "OOOH yes please, can we have that one, can we *!!* can we *!!* ".. She didn't say a word. Mr Breading, quite unaware of our thoughts continued.

"Then there is *Antiandrogen Therapy, Radiation Therapy, Chemotherapy, or Cryosurgery*". The parodied words of the Opera house proprietors in Lloyd Webber's 'Phantom of the Opera' sprang to mind *'Far to big a choice for my taste'*

"What do you recommend?" I asked

"You are only 62" he said. Why does everyone feel this need to tell me how old I am? I fought facetiousness.

"Yes" I said. In a low positive tone

"At your age, I think there is only one real choice" he said

"Yes?", I said again.   This time I allowed my voice to rise slightly hence posing a question.

"It is major surgery" he said

"Yes" I said, taking the word from the roof of my mouth.

"I recommend a *Radical Prostatectomy*." That's easy for you to say, I thought.

"I see", I said, having already infused Yes, with all the colours I was capable of.

"Would you like me to run thought the advantages and disadvantages of each one?".   It was time for me to take control.   I leant back in my seat and crossed my legs, mentally pulling my skirt down over my knees.

"The fact is, Mr Breading",   I said, reaching across to take Polly's hand, and then, finding that my arm was at least two feet too short, changing the action into a vague globally encompassing, though meaningless gesture. "the fact is, that Anne and I have studied the options a little"

"Oh" he seemed surprised.

"On the internet", I explained.

"Oh" he said in a voice that indicated that he was not impressed. "That wretched thing makes experts of everybody" he said. And then pausing continued "but unfortunately it's a case of a little knowledge etc. etc".   He had the control back again.   More quietly I said

"We have decided to take your recommendation, and if you think surgery is the answer for me, we have studied the options, and we agree."

"Do you understand the side effects?" he asked, genuinely anxious that we did.

"Incontinence, and impotence" I said

"Easy to say," he said, "not always so easy to live with."

"I know what both are," I said, "what is the likely severity?"

"Incontinence is unlikely to be anymore than a short term inconvenience," he said. "You will have a catheter for up to three weeks." Your pelvic floor muscles will become weak, and you may experience involuntary dribbling when you cough or when you laugh."

"Whose laughing?" I thought.

"It will be no more that mothers always have to deal with after giving birth. I'm sure you will cope," He paused and placing his elbows on his table steepled his fingers. "if however it becomes a longer term problem, there is a fairly simple surgical procedure I can perform which will strengthen the pelvic floor muscles." I was relieved. Irreverently I had thought we might have to move back to Bexhill where we had spent the first 22 years of our married life. Bexhill, that wonderful Victorian seaside resort of which it was said. *'Bexhill, the town where the elderly come to die.....and then forget what they came for.'* Or, in my case, *'Dover for the continent....Bexhill for the incontinent.'*

"The impotency may prove the greater problem. Perhaps I can explain.   When I open you up to remove your prostate I will be working very close to a bundle of nerves that are responsible for a man obtaining an erection.   If I am lucky, I will be able to remove the prostate without damaging those nerves"   If *YOU* are lucky, I thought.   I said nothing.

"but that may not be possible.   They may be damaged significantly, they may be damaged partially, what you have got to bear in mind is this, when I do this operation my only thought will be to remove ALL the cancer, NOT to protect your future erections".   Don't pussyfoot around, I thought. Just tell it as it is.

"I understand", I said, I looked at Polly, she nodded.....thankfully I thought.   "I, we, would like you to go ahead" I said.   "When can you do it?"

"He opened his desk diary.   Next Wednesday," he said.   Or if that doesn't give you enough time to make arrangements, we could book you in for the following Wednesday".

"I don't want to appear to be taking this less than seriously"   I said, but would I be putting myself at any risk to delay it by one further week to October 12th? That is three weeks Wednesday." I thought he deserved an explanation.   "You see, every year we drive to Tenerife at this time.   There is only one sailing a week from Cadiz to Santa Cruz and you have to book many weeks in advance. We have a booking two weeks Tuesday on the 5th October.   We arrive in Santa Cruz on Thursday 7th, but I can arrange to fly back on that week-end and will be available from the 10th"

"That's a date then" he said "I will arrange for you to be admitted on the evening of the 12th, and put you on my theatre list for first thing on the Wednesday morning, that is the 13th".   He smiled, and I leaned back both in my chair and in short-lived relief.   "But", he began.   Hold on a minute, I thought, you've had your BUT, you had it right at the beginning of the consultation. I said nothing, I just raised a quizzical eyebrow.   "I do need to check that your bladder is clear.   The nurse will take you to one of the treatment rooms, and prepare you, and then I will come along and just pop a camera down 'Old Roger Moffit' and have a look around the inside of your bladder". 'Old Roger Moffit,' what public school did he hail from. I had a passing acquaintance with 'John Thomas,' I knew 'The Old Man', and I'd shaken hands with 'Old Todger' a time or two, but 'Old Roger Moffit' - now he was someone my sheltered upbringing had kept me away from. Having got over that very minor shock, I analysed the rest of his statement. JUST POP A CAMERA DOWN 'OLD ROGER MOFFIT' - now, unless Old Roger was the gardener who was going to stand in for me, that could only mean one thing, and one potentially eye watering thing at that. What, I wondered, are we talking here, Box Brownie or Cannon Digital?. Mr Breading was still speaking, "It will be a little uncomfortable, but shouldn't be too painful."   Well, that obviously ruled out the Box Brownie.   The nurse took me to the treatment room, but first took Polly to a comfortable waiting area, and me to a small, but adequate cubicle within the treatment room. "Take of your clothes and slip the gown on" she said. Well, I'd been here before and was back in the treatment room almost before she could assemble a camera crew.

"That was quick", she said. "just jump up on the couch"

"and face the wall" I thought

"Good, now just lie on your back and make yourself comfortable. Mr Breading wont be a minute." He wasn't.

"Right, old chap, just lie still, I am going to push this flexible tube down the 'Old Fella,' and then rotate it so that I can have a good look around inside". I didn't much like the sound of 'The *Old* Fella , but at least Roger the gardener appeared to have had his marching orders. No more, it had to be said, did I like the look of the 'flexible tube,' which, bearing in mind where it was about to be pushed appeared to be about the size of an alkathene drainpipe.

"It won't take a minute, it will be unpleasant, and you may feel a desperate urge to pee". It didn't, it was, and I did.

"Your bladder looks fine" he said, "no problems at all." You can get dressed now and have a good trip to Tenerife."

"Thank you very much," I said. I'll see you on the 12th. I walked to the door, just as I got there he called softly.

"Oh Mr Jay" I turned

"Yes"

"Any minute now you will feel an uncontrollable urge to pee." He got that right, within seconds I was in a class where I could unsuccessfully *'buttock clench'* for England. For the first time in my life (possibly) I almost failed to reach the porcelain. Luckily, I got through the toilet door, by the skin of my.......teeth, and so the hospital cleaners would have had no overtime that night.

Dressed and dried, I collected Polly and we walked back through reception.

"Oh Mr Jay" it was Georgina, Mr Breading's secretary. "I need to make arrangements for you to have a pre-admission assessment. When will you be available?"

"Well", I said, "today's is Friday, and we set off for Tenerife on Wednesday week."

"Can we book you in next Friday say?",

"Friday will be fine", I said

"At 8 o'clock". I blanched, but said

"a.m. or p.m."

" Oh, most definitely a.m." she said, "we're fitting you in"

"That will be fine" I said. Polly got out her diary.

It had been a long summer. Five important matters still hovered waiting to be addressed. In fact, one important matter to be repeated five times. For twelve weeks Polly and I have kept our roller-coaster summer to ourselves. Now we must share it, and, I am sure, face the wrath of three children, a mother and a business partner who would all want to know why they have been kept in the dark. We planned our campaign like a quasi-military exercise. On Monday week, two days before Polly's Wentworth appearance, I would take Tim to lunch and tell him the story. Three days later we were setting off for Paris and staying the night with Tania and Nigel. Over a Parisian dinner seemed perfect. We are calling in to the Gibraltar office on the following Monday for a board meeting, and, the night before, I would be having dinner in the evening with the group CEO and my business partner. The perfect time. We were due to arrive in Tenerife on the Thursday of that same week and Jem, I know, will have booked a welcome home (winter home) dinner at our favourite restaurant. Not perfect but opportune, particularly as we have to tell him that we are flying back two days later. 'Jobs OXO,' as my old pal Pip Kirby from the isle of Man used to say when a job was done and dusted. But not quite. My mother. Whilst I did not relish telling any of them. I really could not bear the thought of telling my mother. I hoped my reticence was for all the right reasons. Mother is wonderful, but she could *'worry'* for England. Olympic class without a doubt. Things that to me seem inconsequential, will have her tossing and turning the night away. The health of the family, the health of the nation, the rise in crime, the fall in moral standards. All total *'worry worthy'* causes. But just for a moment set aside.   It has to be said that over the past year she has become a million times better, she has developed new and exciting interests, she has met new friends. She goes line-dancing on a Monday, she goes to a wooden spoon club - tea, cakes and gossip - on a Wednesday.   She belongs to a bible class and a rambling club.   The two must never be confused. She is becoming more and more active in the church.   With horizons so broadening, how can I give her news which may, just may, narrow those horizons again because they get in the way of good 'worry time.'   Mum is 84 years old, but unlike the rest of the world, every year she gets a year younger. If anyone didn't know, and most don't, they would put her at early seventies at most *(many friends have asked how I have a mother who looks younger than me)*. I don't want to risk stopping that delightful trend. Polly and I discussed it at length.   We decided to compromise.   We would go to Eastbourne and take mum to lunch at the Mirabelle restaurant in the Grand Hotel.   From there on, we would play it by ear.

Mum was waiting for us in the lobby of the hotel. Full of life, as always. We went through to the restaurant and over first drinks we listened to her news.   Len had been to visit (my late Aunt's brother, and one of my mothers favourites) he meant to stay for a week, but had been taken ill and had to go home. His daughters husband, Neil, who had previously had bowel cancer which was in remission, had suffered a relapse. My Uncle Ted, mum's brother-in law, had prostate cancer. He was 87 and they weren't going to operate. He was very tearful, and on the phone for 40 minutes. Line-dancing was brilliant, and mum was being involved in an ever increasing number of activities in the Church. We talked about the children, we talked about Polly and her remarkable golfing success, we talked about grandson Jack. We talked about Tenerife and mum's intended visit in the new year. After lunch we went back to her small but cosy flat with its panoramic views over Eastbourne and the sea. We sat and drank tea as the dusk fell and the lights of the town flickered on. We talked about golf, crime, family, friends, children, grandchildren, cars, rates, newspapers, television.....somehow cancer never cropped up. Eventually we said our goodbyes and set off for home. As we pulled into the main road Polly looked at me and said "You couldn't tell her could you?"

"No" I said "I couldn't."

I attended the pre-admission examination with a light heart and a ballerinas gait. When I left it looked more like a farmer's gate.

The pre-admission nurse was very nice. As a relatively fit man who had 'no previous guv'nor' I sailed through the questions. She took half an armful of blood to carry out various tests, she took swabs from almost every orifice on account of the fact that I had been seen in an NHS hospital and they were determined to keep MRSA out of the private sector.   My blood pressure was good, my ECG appeared OK, (despite Doctor Meong Liu - or was it Liu Meong) my mental state was almost euphoric ....until.................

"Has Mr Breading explained *all* about the operation to you?"

"I think so, yes"

"It is major surgery, and as such there are always risks"

"Yesss" I was practicing the yes word again.

"A very small percentage - *less* than one in a hundred die during the operation"

DIE DURING THE OPERATION - ONE IN A HUNDRED.   It might be a small per-centage. BUT- *one, in a hundred. ONE IN A BLOODY HUNDRED.* The nurse was still talking.

"And 3 or 4 people who have the operation find that the cancer still spreads, or has already spread, to other parts of the body."   Who is this lady, she should audition as warm-up woman for 'Make 'em Laugh'.

"I know it's all very disturbing," she said,

Ah!, I thought, she knows its very disturbing - that's alright then.

"But it is very important.   Let me give you this booklet." She handed me a booklet produced by the Royal College of Surgeons, and called *PROSTATE CANCER - Questions and Answers.*

"Well, that's us all done Basil, we'll see you on the twelfth."

"Goodbye" I said.   I did not have the heart for a merry quip.

When I got home, I read the booklet.

Page 16.   Are there any risks in a Radical Prostatetectomy.   **Yes.**   Unfortunately **3-4 out of 10 men** having the operation will find that the **cancer has already spread** to other surrounding tissues   thus making the operation ineffective. Fewer than **1 in 100 men die as a result of the operation.**

Ah well, the *die,* if you will forgive the pun, was cast.

On Monday I met my eldest son Tim at 'Le Souffle' restaurant for lunch.   Polly was playing golf and preparing for her big day at Wentworth. Tim was already there when I arrived.

"Hi Dad"

"Hi Tim"

"How's you?"

"I'se OK, How's you?" Our standard greeting. We ordered drinks, Kir Royale for me and Coca Cola for Tim (well he is only 38).   Tim had produced a portfolio of web page designs for a business idea we, the whole family were considering.   After we had read them through together I said.

"I've had a bit of disturbing new Tim"

"Oh", said Tim, cutting straight to the chase, "to do with your foot?"

"Not exactly", I said, and plunged on. "In June I was diagnosed with cancer"

"Of what?" he said, "and why haven't you told me before?"

"Well", I said, "we haven't told anyone, Mum and I wanted to know exactly how serious it was and what treatment was recommended before we worried any of you."

"And?" said Tim.

"Its cancer of the Prostrate, its pretty serious, and I am having a radical prostatectomy two weeks Wednesday."

"We'll talk about this again" he said, and then, "What do you think of this design?" he pointed at a page in the portfolio and seemingly the subject was closed, but, I knew that within ten minutes of walking back through his front door he was going to log on to the internet, and by evening he would know as much about Prostate cancer as I did. It was then that the questions would start. Before I left Tim, I told him that, on no account must he tell his brother or sister. This was news that had to come from me.

Before we set of for Paris we had the highlight of our summer ahead of us. Polly at Wentworth. The two days we spent there deserves a book on its own. Instead I will just give you the highlights. The LGU and the sponsors looked after the girls and their partners as if we were on the professional tour circuit. We were booked into a splendid hotel suite which, had we been there on our own account would have cost £350 per night. The arrangements at the course were absolutely first class, and the Gala Dinner was held in the club itself, and was sumptuous.   Polly played very well on a course designed for people who hit the ball twice as far as the average club golfer.   The television cameras followed us all the way around, and after a magnificent bunker shot at the 18th, Polly stepped of the green to be met by both TV and Radio microphones asking for a two minute interview.   This was an event experienced by so few at club level, and, apart from a tape of the interviews, we have a wonderful photograph of Polly standing beside the large *'Leader Board'* and pointing to her name under the heading *'LADY AMATEUR GOLF CLUB CHAMPIONSHIP OF GREAT BRITAIN AND IRELAND.'*   For an amateur club golfer it doesn't get any better, and those two days will, without a doubt, remain the highlight of Polly's golfing life.

The day following Wentworth we set off for Paris and arrived at around 5pm on Wednesday. Jack was allowed to join us at the dinner table and we enjoyed his company for a while as we enjoyed our aperitifs. After he had been put to bed we talked inconsequential small talk for a while longer, and then Nigel filled our wine glasses and brought in the first course.   I didn't pussyfoot around.

"I've got something to tell you both" I said. "in June I was diagnosed with prostate cancer and I am having a radical prostatechtomy on Wednesday week."   Tania was cross,

"And how come we didn't know about it until now?" I stuck to the party line.   We quite spoiled the dinner by talking about what Prostates do and how they are removed.   Nigel thought I was taking it very calmly. but I didn't tell them about the Tigers.   They arranged to come to England to visit the week-end after the operation.   The second hurdle had been successfully jumped.   I knew that yet another computer would be busy that night.   We left Paris the next day, having passed on to Tania the same instruction - not to tell her younger brother.

We had a wonderful relaxing drive through France and Spain.   The first night we stayed in a small hotel in Bordeaux.   An earlyish stop, a relaxing bath euphoric in the knowledge that we had got two fifths of the way through our self-imposed task without actual bloodshed.   The second night we crossed into Spain and stayed in the wonderful medieval town of Toledo.   We booked a suite in a Parador high on the hill overlooking the distant town with its magnificent Gothic Cathedral.   The evening was delightful, warm and balmy.   After we had eaten we sat on the balcony long into the night. A bottle of champagne and a deliciously chilled bottle of Chablis, accompanied us as we enjoyed the peace and the tranquillity of a medieval city that had been the witness of far greater problems than ours.   We reviewed our life together and the future ahead of us.   I felt totally at peace and ready for anything that was to come.

For so long as I live, that evening on a balcony overlooking Toledo will stay with me amongst the fondest memories in my memory box.

We had one further stop in Spain, and reached Gibraltar on the Saturday evening. That night we had dinner in the Elliot Hotel and I told Sharron the news. Like the children she was very cross to have been kept in the dark, but showed great concern for us and what the future held. Polly and I had a free day on Sunday and we took a taxi ride all over the rock. The caves, the Barbary apes and the harbour. A peaceful day, spent in bright sunshine in a time capsule which, for the moment, for us, did not stretch beyond October 13th. Another memory to cherish. The board meeting took place on Monday. We did not tell our fellow directors, nor, of course, the staff, and by mid-afternoon on Monday we had crossed the border back into Spain and headed for Cadiz and the ferry to Tenerife.

We reflected that they had all taken the news with outward calm. They all were a little angry that we had gone a whole summer without sharing our worries. But we knew, that pretty much without exception they had all rushed home to their computers, and within hours of receiving the news had almost certainly collectively known, as much about Prostates as the combined bands of the Royal Medical Corps.

After a calm and peaceful voyage, we arrived at Santa Cruz on Thursday late afternoon and were at our home in the South of the Island by early evening.   Jem, as we expected had booked us a table at Bacchus, one of our favourite restaurants. We were now pretty accomplished and, once again, did not beat about the bush.   Jem, like the others was cross to have been kept in the dark, but understanding for the reasons.   He did however have questions, asked thoughtfully and with concern, as is his way.   He also felt for us having had a seven day trip to get to Tenerife, now facing a two day stay over and a plane back to where we started from.

Our flight was OK.   We took off, we flew, and we landed and by the week-end of the 10th October, I was ready to face whatever was to be faced.   We had a restful week-end.   We continued our talk of things we had done and things we had yet to do.   We had a lunch at the golf club and a dinner at 'Le Souffle.'   In some curious way we were far to close to D Day for the Tigers to have any relevance.

At lunch time on Tuesday 12th October, Polly and I decided to have a 'final' (for the time being) lunch in the familiar and much loved surroundings of 'The Lime Tree' our own local restaurant overlooking the village square.   We sat at our window table in the corner. The table that had shared so many of our summer thoughts. I had barely sipped my first Kir Royale when John, one of the proprietors came and stood over us. "Basil,

Polly" he said "What are you doing here, I thought you'd gone back Tenerife?"

"We had" I answered, "but I have had to come back for a small operation"

"Oh dear" said John. "on the foot again?"

"Not this time" I said

"The knee?"

"No"

"You haven't got trouble with the hip have you?"

"John", I said, "before you run out of body parts would you like me to tell you?".

" I wasn't being nosy" he said

"No?" I questioned

"Yes?" he said

"I have come back for a *Radical Prostatectomy*" that will shut him up I thought. I was wrong, it simply opened flood gate number two.

"Oh no". he said, "funnily enough I was talking to a doctor friend about that very operation yesterday. He said he wouldn't recommend that operation, even as a last resort"

"Thank you for sharing that John" I said. He was unfazed.

"He said its major surgery and has terrible side effects."

"I know" I said

"Incontinence" he said

"Possibly" I answered

"Impotence" he said

"Maybe" I agreed

"And it is far too invasive" he said. I had to turn this around.

"For my surgeon," I said, " it is so common he carries them out two at a time using only a Swiss army knife and a ball of string." John slapped his thigh.

"Basil," he chortled, "You're one in a hundred." ONE IN A HUNDRED. DA DA DA DA...BOOOM DA DA DA DA BOOOM, DA DA DA DA DA DE DA DA. The opening chorus of Carmen Buranda crashed into my head. Across the square, gazing steadily at the restaurant window, I knew Damien, - The Omen - would be watching.

CHAPTER 17
MY BLACK AND BLUE FRIEND

OCTOBER 2004

We finished our lunch. I waved to Damien, dismissed the Carmen Buranda Choir, shook hands with, a still unrepentant, John, and walked home to pack my little bag.

We arrived at the Winterlands Hospital at 5.30 p.m. on the evening of the 12th October. "Basil Jay reporting for duty" I said. The ward clerk was already there to greet me and take me to my room. I was a little surprised to be shown into a two bedded room, with a number of monitors dotted around. "Am I not in a single room", I asked, half wondering whether the insurance company had asked for table d'ote instead of al la carte.

"Only for the first night or two" the ward clerk smiled "immediately after the operation we have to keep a close eye on you" she indicated the monitors. "When everything is OK you will go into one of the private rooms".

"I understand" I said.

"Originally you were going to have this room to yourself tonight, but there is an emergency down in Theatre now, and the lady will be coming into this room after the operation. Perhaps I better find another room for you if you are going to have a good nights sleep"

"That will be good" I said, "I have a big day tomorrow" The ward clerk left us, only to return after just a few minutes to say

"Room 14 is empty, I think we will pop you in there." The room was small, but comfortable. It had a shower with a seat, but no bath. A small table, and two comfortable chairs. It was going to be fine for my last night as the possessor of a Prostate. Sonika came in.

"Halloo", she said in a broad South African drawl, "I'm Sonika, welcome to Winterlands, I just have to ask you a few questions and then I will leave you in peace."

You leave me in peace tonight, I thought, and Mr Breading leaves me in pieces tomorrow. I nodded and said "fire away then."

"OK" the voice rising on the K in the South African way. "Your name is Basil Jay."

"I know," I said

"I see, we have a clever clogs do we" said Sonika

"Sorry" I said,

"and you were born on 28th July 1942"

"I was" I said

"Have you any allergies?"

"Brussel Sprouts bring me out in a rash" I pulled a face.

"Behave yourself," she wagged her finger, "You know what I mean"

I tried to look repentant. "Not that I know of" I said

"Have you ever suffered from?" The list appeared endless, and most of the answers were NO. Once again I speculated, how could I be so well, and feel so fit, and yet be facing a major, life threatening operation.

"That was easy" drawled Sonika. "I am just going to take your blood pressure and then I will leave you in peace" That phrase again. My blood pressure was 130 over 80 which just underlined my earlier thought.

After Sonika had gone, Polly unpacked my two pairs of pyjamas and dressing gown, put my slippers under the chair, my wash bag in the bathroom, and then packed my day clothes back in the bag. "You won't be needing these for a few days, she said, so I will take them home."

We sat quietly for about an hour. I could hear the nurse's beginning to make their 'pill' rounds and, as I wanted to write a few letters, I suggested that Polly return to the comfort of our own home, and some of me would see her on the morrow. We both knew tomorrow would be a cake walk, but the goodbye somehow held the possibility of, that *'one in a hundred.'*

Polly hadn't gone long when a new nurse came in, very brisk, very nice, but very business like. "Have you had a decent shave?" she nodded her head "down there"

"Well, I have", I said, but I was not quite sure just how much was needed?". "Mr Breading likes a lot of room to work" said nursie, "best to shave from just under your ribs, to just above your knees, I'll get you a couple of razors." Well, the fact was, I had done nothing like enough. I had shaved with difficulty, from my belly button to my hairy bits, having assessed by reference to the diagrams in *'Prostates, all you need to know'* exactly where I would make the 2" incision if I was the surgeon. Nursie came back.

"How long is the incision likely to be" I asked gingerly, not really wanting to know the answer.

"Usually between 8 and 10 inches" she said.

"Ouch" I said

"Don't be silly" she said, "you'll be fast asleep," then briskly

"Here's a couple of razors. Let me give you a tip, it's much easier to shave dry, so leave the shaving foam in the can." After she had left me alone, I wandered into the bathroom, stripped off, and looked at my relatively hairy visage for the last time (at least for a while). Nursie was quite right about the ease of a dry shave, and the curly belly hair, and the equally curly hairs over my thighs, down to my knees soon fell beneath the safety razors blade.   I stopped about four inches above the knee and stood and looked.   There I was, looking for all the world like a participant in the *'Rocky Horror Show'* I appeared to be wearing black stockings which terminated at white, and silky smooth, thighs.   Of the rest, imagination must suffice.

Nursie came back.   "Have you shaved?" she asked,

"Yes", I answered, "from the top to the bottom just as you asked."

"Good for you" she said as if I had just won the lottery, "as I said, Mr Breading likes a bit of room to work."

"What are you wearing?" she said suddenly.

"My new Jim Jams" I answered - "bought specially for the occasion - not a garment I have a lot of use for at home."

"You can keep them on tonight" she said, "but tomorrow morning I want you to put on this gown" she held out one of the awful gowns of recent front loading memory.

"it's one of those gowns" I said.

"Think of it as a nightie" she answered.   And I did, for ever more

"Nur-penny" I said, starting to say nurse and then spotting her name tab Penny"

"Nurpenny" she said, "what sort of name is that".   The ice was broken.

"I've been reading the Daily Mail"

"Whose a clever boy then?"

"No, seriously Penny, look at this article"   I showed her the headline.

BREAKTHROUGH IN PROSTATE SURGERY.   *'I was playing golf just three weeks after a radical prostatectomy says Ian, and I don't even have a scar.'*

"Should I mention it to Mr Breading?" I asked. Penny put her chin on her ample bosom, and looked up at me over her glasses.   "Poor, poor boy," she said "why don't you get some sleep?" Sleep, however, for me, was not yet an option. Remembering, though trying not to, pre-admission Carole's *'one in a hundred '* message, I had to tell the people who were important to me things I had never told them before.   My letters were, of course, to my mother, who thought I was on a deck chair in the Canary islands rather than an operating theatre in Kent.   For her a message of love about my childhood, and thanks for her constant presence thereafter.   Polly, from whom I had no secrets, but for whom I still had a message to see her through another 25 or so years.   My children, who between them had, individually given me both the best times and the worst times of my life, but who, without exception, had, in the end, done so much to make me proud.   Sharron, who had reminded me of the energy I had had at forty.   Who had made my, now *our* business grow in a way that gave me all the excitement of the chase with none of bruises of the falls.   Hardly into my self appointed task I had a visitor.   "Hello, my friend, can I come in?"

"Of course," I said

"My name is Dr. Mappa, I am to be your anaesthetist tomorrow."

"Good evening" I said

"Can I ask you are few questions?" he said, "I will try not to take up too much of your valuable time." He eyed my Basildon Bond writing pad, and Caron D'Arche pen lying in readiness upon the table.

"I am all yours" I said

"You will be tomorrow" he smiled. "Now, are you allergic to anything?"

Apart from questions, I thought, "Not to my knowledge" I said.

"Do you suffer from shortness of breath" he said

"I can't run a marathon in two hours" I said, "but generally I think I'm OK"

"Can you walk up Gabriel's Hill without panting?" I was not quite sure where Gabriel's Hill was. I took a chance

"I expect so, I said

"Good.......good...........goooooooood" his voice petered out.

"Now, a few basic questions, I expect you've already been asked them a time or two." He proceeded to ask me a few basic questions, but I'd already been asked them a time or two.

When the questions were over Dr Mappa stood up, stretched ostentatiously, and said. "That's it, Mr Breading wants you first on his list tomorrow, so I would guess they will wheel you down about

9.0 o'clock." He walked to the door and turned. "is there anything you want to ask me?"

"Do I need to cancel my 2 o'clock tee time?" I asked. He clearly considered my question frivolous. He merely smiled and said,

"See you in the morning then, sleep well." Sleep was still a long way away. I sat down to my letters, six letters which I hoped, and *frankly* did not believe that anyone would ever read. Except me of course, and I read them and re-read them all several times before I sealed them with a falling tear and the passing thought *"by gum but 'ee writes a champion letter."* I tucked them in the case of my CD walkman where they would be easily found if they needed to be found, and yet were suitable concealed if they did not. Feeling at ease, I climbed into bed. Told the Tigers not to even think about it, and quite quickly sunk into a deep, but dream encrusted sleep.

It must have been 30 years since I last saw my old friend Tony Brindle (You remember his brother Billy) well, 30 years since I'd seen him, and probably 25 since I'd even thought about him. And yet, there he was, knocking on my door wearing a white tuxedo and pink bow tie (Tony always was a bit dapper). "Basil, me old friend," he said, me and the kids here have come to give you a treat." I looked at his companions. Standing wreathed in smiles were my three children, Tim, Tania and Jeremy. But, things were not quite right. Tony B was at my wedding. I was almost 22 at the time, and he was less than a year older. Yet here he was at my door, pink bow tie and all, accompanied by my three children, - except, he was still 22, and they were, well, at the very least a decade older. I went with the flow.

"We have a surprise for you," said Tony B. A new restaurant has opened at the top of Gabriel's Hill, it is called BASILO'S and they make a Kir Royale to die for." I don't recall making any comment, simply following them along a road where the water got deeper and deeper until it was swirling around my waist. "Don't worry about the water," said Tony B, "bit of flood, but it will soon be gone when we reach Gabriel's Hill." I didn't worry about the water, and as I looked at them all I noted that their feet were visible and dry. I looked down, water was still swirling around my waist. Tony B took my arm and we were soon walking up Gabriel's Hill. Except now, the three children were making it hard work, because whilst Tony B was pulling me forward, they were dragging me backwards...and winning. Tony B let go of my arm and marched forward. "Don't lag you lot," he called. "Soon be there, just at the top of Gabriel's Hill, Basilo's a restaurant with Kir Royales to die for." Hang on a minute. Gabriel was a bloody angel, what am I doing climbing his hill. And what the dickens is Basil doing with a restaurant called BASILO'S, and A KIR ROYALE TO DIE FOR. You're having a laugh, Tony B, I'm out of here. The last I saw of Tony B, he had turned, was pointing back down the hill and calling "Watch

how you go through the *Lake of Incontinence.*"
He was gone, and I woke up, still in room 14 in
Winterlands Hospital.   *Funny things Dreams.*
Bring back the Tigers.

It is an offence in Hospital to sleep after 6.30.
So, anxious to please, I awoke with the lark.
Penny was still on duty.

"Good morning Basil" she said, "Sorry I can't
offer you a cup of tea, but you can go and have
a good shower and a shave any time you like.
There is no need to worry you much this morning,
as long as we have you all ready for about 8.0
o'clock because Mr Breading will be calling into
see you, and probably the anaesthetist as well."
I had a vague impression that she had split her
infinitive.... But who cares on a sunny morning, and
anyway , it didn't really show.

"Thank you Penny", I said "I will make sure
I am ready" and I was, with at least half an hour
to spare.

"Good morning Mr Jay" It was Dr Mappa "Did
you sleep well?"

"Very thank you," I was sure he would not be
interested in the Hill of Gabriel or the Lake of
Incontinence.

"I will just talk you through what we plan to
do." Before he could continue Mr Breading came
in and left no-one in any doubt as to who was the
boss.

"How are you this morning?" he said hugely,
"I'm fine" I replied, small-ly

154

"I just have to have you sign the consent form" he said "just here" he added, pointing

"Just there?" I said also pointing,

"That's the ticket" he said "removing the piece of paper as soon as my pen had grazed the surface.   "I'll be ready for you in about an hour, any questions?"   I almost didn't dare, and the question of the revolutionary keyhole surgery was clearly an absolute no no.

"No.......em....No" I said.

"That's the ticket.   Just do as Dr Mappa tells you and you will be back in your ward before you know it.   See you in an hour"

"He's a good surgeon" said the nurse and Dr Mappa together as he powered out of my room.

"Much more important than the social graces" I thought, hopefully.

After a while I was left in peace.   Unbeknown to me, an emergency had just been admitted.   It was not an hour.   In fact I was not taken down to surgery until just after eleven o'clock.   But, I didn't know that then.

I didn't read, I didn't turn on the television, I just lay there and thought.   It was October 13th (thankfully not a Friday - not you understand that I am the least bit superstitious, anyway it wouldn't have mattered if it was a Friday, I'd remembered to say White Rabbits on the first of the month).   I thought about many things in the hour that I waited to be summoned.   Most of all I thought about all the things Polly and I had not done, and just hoped that we would have time to do them. I suppose, my prevailing motto coming forth from the preceding 24 hours, was I must *'make the most'*. I *must make the most of* my children, my grandson (and hopefully others to follow) my mother, my wife and my time. My time multiplied by all the above. More time for Polly and I, more time for Mother and I, more time for Tim, for Tania and for Jem. BUT. Only as much time as they want of me, NOT as much time as I want of them. I want to make the most of the excitement of watching OCTOPUS (my old company) grow, and its new offshoots of WILLOW and PRIMESPOT. When Polly and I were young we were adventurous. For goodness sake we drove three children aged between 2 and 7 across the sub continent of India when we were in our early thirties and had no money. But, for years we have done so little. These things must change. I *must make the most of life*. Over the past 3 months I have ranged between believing I would live forever, and doubting that I'd make the week-end. Whatever time is left, and if the man upstairs hasn't been too offended by my life, it could hopefully be another twenty years or so, BUT, whether twenty years or twenty days from now on *not a day will be wasted*.

A recalled a poem I had read, sometime, somewhere. It was called 'Time Passing,' and the words had stayed with me.

When I was a babe, I laughed and wept
Time crept
When I was a youth I thought and talked
Time walked
When I was a full-grown man
Time ran
As each day I older grew
Time flew
Soon, like all, I will pass on
Time gone

"Hello Basil, I'm Sue."   I came out of my reverie

"Good morning Sue."

"I have the lovely job of looking after you until 8.30 tonight, by which time I expect to see you peeing for England." The comment was lost on me, then, but later that night was to have deep deep meaning. "But for now, get yourself out of bed.   You have an appointment with a surgeon, and at this end of the operation you are fit enough to walk to Theatre." Was I offended that a nurse could treat a patient this way. NO I was not. Sue's cheery countenance and happy manner made the day seem normal, and what was about to happen the cake walk I had been promised.   I POPPED on my gown, I POPPED on my dressing gown, I POPPED on my slippers, and matching Sue step for jaunty step I followed her down the corridor to the Theatre.

"This is Basil" , she said to the theatre nurse, "look after him" She smiled at me, I will be here when you wake up" she said, "and make sure you behave yourself."   With a wink, she was gone.

I love the bit when the anaesthetist says, "Right, just a little prick in the back of your hand, and I want you to count backwards from 10, slowly. Keep your eyes open so that I know you're awake". You feel the prick, ten, nine...you make your eyes stare at the light above your head....eig...

"How are you Basil?" It was Sue, "It's all over, you are fine.   You're in recovery, you've been here about 45 minutes, and I've come to take you back to your room.   But this time I won't make you walk"   but then, things started to go awry. Another voice.

"Blood Pressures dropping.........90 over 70." Sue, stepped back and another nurse in overalls stepped forward and took my hand.

"Don't worry Basil," she said everything is fine.

"85 over 62" said the voice

"Where's Mr Breading?" just voices, could belong to anyone.

"He's gone" - I *hoped* they were talking about Mr Breading.

"Try upstairs, ask reception if he's left the building."

"78 over 55"

"It's the wound, it must be bleeding inside."

"Don't worry Basil, everything is fine" I didn't care, I was still in that wonderful euphoric state where the world drifts by and you're not part of it. It could have been an episode of Holby City.

"70 over 48"

"Reception said he left five minutes ago, they're trying his mobile"

"is Dr Mappa here?"

"I'll get him."

"65 over 45."

"Reception said his mobile's switched off or has no signal."

"Dr Mappa, it's, Mr Jay, his wound seems to be bleeding, His BP is dropping."

"Where's Mr Breading?"

"He's gone.   Everything was fine, the bleed must have started when we tried to move him to the porter's trolley."

"You'll be fine Basil, wont be long and we'll get you upstairs."

"60 over 40" I think I was feeling a bit cold, but what the hell.   Dr Mappa gave a number of instructions, most sounded incomprehensible. "Some black silk," I heard him say. I didn't understand, perhaps he was going to knit me a pair of socks to keep my legs warm.

"48 over 27."

I felt a pin prick in my arm.   I must have dozed off.   Sue was patting my hand.   "Well, she said, perhaps we can try again, I might of guessed I'd have trouble with you."   I could tell by her smile that she didn't mean it.

"90 over 70 Doctor."

"I'd like to see it over 100 before he goes up."

"Sorry Sue, can you give us another fifteen minutes." Sue, gave my hand a final pat.

"I'll see you in a minute." All the activity seemed to have finished. Dr Mappa, leaned over me.

"How do you feel Basil?"

"OK" I said, " a little woozy."

"There's no problem" he said, "Your wound started bleeding inside, but I have re-stitched it and everything seems good now. I just want to get your blood pressure up and bit and then we can get you up to your room."

"95 over 72."

"There, its getting better every minute." He looked across at an unseen nurse. "You can call the ward again, it will be fine by the time they get here." I closed my eyes.

"Back again. " It was Sue, "perhaps you can drag yourself away this time."

"99 over 72"

"OK nurse, you can take him away." Sue walked by my side holding my hand. A young man dressed in green was pushing the trolley keeping up a one sided dialogue with Sue on every conceivable subject from holidays to reality programmes on television, to the quality of the hospital food. He made the day seem normal. As we came out of the lift, an attractive lady in a red blouse and black skirt was standing in a small waiting area, just outside of the two bedded monitoring room.

"Hello," said Sue, "can I help?".   From a distance I heard a voice mention my name.   "He's here on the trolley," said Sue, "you are just in time." I had drips in my arms, epidurals in my back, oxygen mask over my face, catheters, well, where they put catheters.   And my first thought as Polly followed me into the room was "Well, at least the testosterone still works."

Polly didn't stay.   They hooked me up to a machine which measured my blood pressure, pulse beat, heart rate, oxygen, and all other vital signs every few minutes.   Sue, busied herself around me like a mother hen, taking, I thought at the time an unhealthy interest in the rate at which my catheter bag filled up.   But a combination of Tramadol, and Epidural put me past caring for the rest of the day and most of the night to follow.   I was conscious every 7 minutes or so of the sleeve on my arm pulsing up as my blood pressure was taken.   The monitor was facing me and I took a vaguely academic interest, whenever I happened to be facing it, in a blood pressure that seemed to range between 91 over 76 and 146 over 104.   A pulse rate that sometimes glided along at around 45 and others fairly galloped at 125.   I was comforted that the old days when what was happening to you was a secret, appeared to have gone. I had been conscious from time to time of a tall slender young lady in a white coat taking a definite interest in me.   Sue had long since gone of duty, and been replaced by Jo and Alison, with back-up from the ward sister Katherine.   The night was surrealistic.   I awoke at one stage to find Alison, fumbling about beneath the covers. She did not break stride when she noticed my eyes were open, she carried on tenderly squeezing a cool pad over my catheter invaded regions whilst saying with a quiet smile. "Your poor little friend is all black and blue."   Well, I couldn't quite recall asking any of my little friends to stay.   That's one to sort out in the morning.   Some hours later I awoke to find a semi-circle of attractive ladies standing by my bed all looking at the tube which led from my little black and blue friend, to a plastic bag hanging on the bed frame.   The lady in the white coat, seemed to be leading the way.

"How much?" she asked

"Only 17 mil in two hours" Katharine replied

"I want to see at least 40 mil an hour" said lady white coat.

"He's very swollen" said Alison, "He must be very sore"

"No, the epidural will keep the pain away" said lady white coat, who then, looking up saw that I was lying there watching them.

"Hello Basil" she said, "I'm Kim, I'm the RMO."

"Hello Kim," I said dreamily, not really caring very much who she was.

"You must think it's bizarre" she said, "a group of grown women standing around a man's bedside, waiting for him to wee"

"And then getting quite excited when he does" added Jo

"You've got to do better" said Kim. "I need to see 40 mil an hour, you've managed just 17 mil in the past two hours."

"Sorry," I said, not really having the slightest idea what I could do about it.

"What time is it?", I asked

"About midnight" said Jo, but don't you worry about that.   In between the warning beeps that the drip was empty, the insistent pips of the monitor when the pulse reader slipped off my finger, and the grip the sleeve as my blood pressure was taken, I slipped into and out of sleep.   One o'clock, two o'clock, three o'clock.   Whenever I awoke it seemed that Doctor Kim was looking at my plastic bag, or delving under the covers looking at my little black and blue friend.   She always smiled when she saw my eyes open, and said "Go to sleep Basil, everything's going just fine."

A cheerful lady brought me a cup of tea at about 6.30.   A sad faced Jo said, "I'm sorry Basil, that's a mistake, Mr Breading says nil by mouth until he's seen you."

At 7.30, another helper, a tall attractive blonde lady, of semi-mature years, brought me a Daily Mail.   I was feeling a bit chipper by now.   "Have you checked I'm not 'Nil by Eyes?" I asked, "I'm Nil by just about everything else, including Hanky Panky."   She laughed and said "Lets take a chance shall we?"

"What on?" I asked "the Daily Mail or the Hanky Panky." I looked at her smugly.

"Stop looking at my smugly" her eyes said as she wagged her finger at me in a 'naughty naughty' sort of way.

Jo came to say goodbye, she had finished her night duty, completed the hand-over and was going home to bed.

"Hello Basil, I'm Debbie, I'll be looking after you today."

"Hello Debbie, how am I?" this time it wasn't a joke.

"Well, you appear to have lived through the night" she said. Don't you just love them. They take away every bit of self-pity you may want to feel even before it can start. "But you're still only half filling your bag with Claret."

"Claret?" I mouthed, uncomprehending

"Claret" she echoed. "Let me tell you our little code. I'm talking about your wee. Now, you've had a nasty bit of surgery and there will be bleeding for a few days. The more you bleed, the redder your wee - just like Claret. After a few days it will begin to look like a nice Rose wine, or, I understand in your case, a Kir Royale. By the time you're ready to go home, you'll be weeing Chardonnay."

"Claret, Kir Royale, Chardonnay" I said, "I'll never think of table wine the same way again."

The morning progressed. Breakfast came and went for many, for me, not even a drink of water. The lady who had been an emergency the night before was in the opposite bed to me, albeit we were both well shielded by curtains. As the morning progressed, so did she. By lunchtime she had been moved to her own room. I was still failing to produce 40 mil per hour of any vintage, and thus was destined to stay in the observation room. Lunch didn't come, but lunch-time and Dr Kim did.

"What are you doing here?" I said, "it's the middle of the day."

"I work here" she said, and your still not producing enough Claret."

"I don't seem to be in control of that function." I said.

"You're not," she said, "but sadly, neither are your kidneys."

"Have you got a sister or were you here last night at one o'clock" I asked her,

"One o'clock, two o'clock, three o'clock, four o'clock," she said, "and all because of your wretched under performing kidneys." The smile made it obvious that she was worried and not angry.

"How come you're still working?", I asked.

"I'm on twenty-four hour call, I manage to get my head down between problems."

"Tell you what," I said, "Take the rest of the day off, I'll call you if I need you." Then Polly arrived, and suddenly I didn't need anybody else.

"You're awake," she said, "You look a bit more cheerful than last time I saw you." she looked great.

"We have a treat in store" I said

"Oh"

"I was given a daily paper, and I noticed that the World Match play from Wentworth starts today. Four hours a day of golf from the championship golf course you now know like the back of your hand."

"Oh that's good" she said.   For Polly television was made for live golf.

Despite the fact we were in the observation room, the nurses set us up the television, and we sunk ourselves into the days 36 hole battles.   It is tempting to give you a blow by blow account of the four days golf.   I wont, suffice it to say that we watched each day and Ernie Els won in the end. For both of us it was riveting to watch the worlds best play the holes that we had become so familiar with.   It was also fascinating to realize that not once, but several times, Tim had put his drive in much the same position as these world leaders, drives, which, for the record, are approximately twice as far as mine.

And so it was that the worst was over, the operation and the first night had been lived through.   My letters could remain un-read, the thoughts they contained my thoughts and mine alone. I now faced just a few days in the care of these wonderful and humorous girls before I would be back home and preparing for Tenerife and a winter in the sun.   At least, that's what I thought.

CHAPTER 18
PLANS FOR A BLUE TRAIN

OCTOBER 2004

Thursday night passed slowly, as did the Claret. The main different between Thursday and Wednesday was that I was rather more aware of what was going on. This sadly meant that I was also much more aware of the fact that I had a thumping head-ache, brought on we later discovered by an aversion to Tramadol. Whereas on night one the regular checking of the vital signs had been, for me, a vague and distant distraction - now, even though the time lapse had been extended from every 7 minutes to every 15 minutes, the whole process had become a definite annoyance. Everybody seemed, as the night progressed, to become more relaxed about my *'bag filling capabilities'*, I suspect I was still far from Olympic standard, but at least I was reasonable club level.

In addition, as the night progressed into the early morning, mounting excitement suggested that I was gradually distilling the Claret down to a strong Kir Royale. My night nurse's sympathised with my headache, but beyond a couple of paracetamol were unable to offer any particular solution.

Around 2 o'clock in the morning I began to suffer from acute discomfort in the 'bladder region' and desperately needed the loo. But that was absurd, I had a tube which quite removed the need for conscious thought. I tried to put it out of my head, concentrated on ignoring my unrelenting headache, and tried to sleep. Another half an hour was all I could manage. But I didn't have to. Through half closed eyelids I saw Dr Kim once more at my bedside. Did the girl never sleep? The nurse was telling her that my Kir Royale emission had fallen to a standstill.

"Basil."

"What are you doing here, you should be in bed?"

"Don't go there" she said "Tell me instead, do you feel any discomfort?"

"Well," I replied, "I have this illusion that I want to go to the loo"

"It's not an illusion" said Kim, "you've got a blood clot in the catheter."

"And a bloody clot in the bed," I said, "who thought the pain was all in the head."

"No", smiled Kim, "it's definitely in the bladder". I liked this young lady, I might even marry her if she asks me and Polly doesn't mind me having two wives. I told her so. "We'll see about that later" she said. "right now I'm going to give you a bladder flush."   Now, there's romantic. I can hear them at the Golf Club - "And tell me Basil, how did you meet your *spare* wife."

"Oh I remember it well, she gave me a bladder flush and I was quite swept away."

The process is not difficult, it is vaguely unpleasant and appears to require a fair amount of bicep power (Dr Kim's, not mine - to be clear... Dr Kim's biceps - my bladder).   A syringe, of a size used to sedate elephants, is filled with sterile water and then injected, DOWN your little friend (to use Alison's vernacular) into the bladder.   A bladder, I might add that has already passed the stage of being *'comfortably full'* .   The water is cold, and the shock is colder.   Once empty, the operator, in this case the slender Dr Kim, reverses the process and pulls, by suction, the water back into the syringe.   The theory is, that when the syringe is full the flow diverts back into the catheter and the waiting bag.   The bigger the blood clot, the harder the effort required. The first flow back into the syringe, is of course the volume of water that left it in the first place. For example, 100 mil in 100 mil out followed by the blood clot.   Basic physics.   Wrooooong. 100 mil in, 100 mill out followed by...... nothing.

Process repeated, then repeated again, and again. Imagine you are positively bursting, you could not cope with another teardrop in your protesting bladder, and then whoosh 100 mil in the wrong direction. By now Dr. Kim was as red in the face as I was. And then the break through, the water went from water coloured to slightly pink, then blushingly pink, then positively red. The blood clot had broken up, the retained volumes gushed forth like the white (well, perhaps pink) water rapids of the Orinoco, and, in a gush, the pain had subsided. Both mine and Dr. Kim's. I was to have at least another half dozen *'Bladder Flushes'*, before the catheter was removed, but none so traumatic as that first night.

"Good Night Basil," said Kim, "try to go to sleep now"

"Good Night Kim....you too." She walked towards the door.

"Oh and Kim" she turned back towards the bed.

"Thank you." I closed my eyes, my headache had nearly gone.

The early morning tea passed me by. The early morning nurse didn't. I had became accustomed to my obs. (observations), and even to the changing of my dressing which appeared to be a four-hourly affair on account of the fact the wound was still leaking a mixture of fluid and blood which made a fairly unpleasant mess on both the dressing, my gown, and the bedclothes. At 6.30 on the Friday morning, two days after the operation and one day after Bernard Langer had unceremoniously disposed of world No. 1, Vijay Singh in the world match play championship a new problem thrust itself upwards.

"Good morning Basil, before I go off duty I want to change your dressing."

It was Penny, one of the nurses who had attended at my first bladder flushing ceremony. She pulled down the sheet and pulled up my gown. My stomach resembled a balloon. It was almost perfectly round, and it was as tight as a drum. "I think I better give Kim a call" said Penny, "Poor girl, didn't get up to bed until about 5 o'clock" I raised my eyebrows "just you lie still I wont be a minute". Kim must have been sleeping on her feet, because she was in my room within just two or three minutes. "I see you're still giving trouble" she said

"Sorry, your sleep has been disturbed" I answered. She just shook her head and busied herself with the stethoscope before tapping her fingers on the tightened skin as if she was playing a drum.

"You have a *paralysed aorli*' " she said. "It's quite common, but in means that your bowels are not working at all and you are absolutely full of wind."

"Your not the first one to tell me that" I said.

"Now then, we had all hoped that today you would come off of 'Nil by Mouth' but now there is no chance until you get that dispelled and your bits functioning properly."

"Well, the good news" I said, "is that it won't do my diet any harm."

And so I entered into two or three days of unspeakable administrations to remove the wind. There could be nothing else, as by now I had had nothing but sips of water and a saline drip for several days. In the event it was EIGHT DAYS before a morsel of food (if such a description is adequate for a bowl of tomato soup) passed my lips, and then it passed them twice. Once on the way in, and once on the way back out again.

That double taste followed a joyous daily ritual of suppositories and enemas, which, from the nurses point of view endorsed the age old saying. *It is much more blessed to GIVE than to RECEIVE.*

This treatment, so joyously administered, was not, I have to tell you the whole of the fun I endured during the seven days following the operation. The wound, that had given so much anxiety in the recovery room got steadily worse. I would make each morning with a damp and pink stained nightie, lying on damp and pink stained sheets. Not, I hasten to add that the girls allowed this to happen. My nightie was on and off more often than a hookers knickers. My bed changed more often than a politicians principles.   In the end, Mr Breading was called.   It was Tuesday, exactly seven days from my admission, and six full days since my operation.   He examined my drum, playing a skilful, though short, tattoo in E minor. He examined my wound. Then, turning to the nurse said.

"Pour some local anesthetic in the wound, take out the top dozen clips, then wheel him down to one of the treatment rooms." He turned to me "Well, Basil, its not healing quite as it should. You're a big chap" - when your just 5 foot 7½ that normally means 'a fat chap' - "and I think the strain of you blowing up like a balloon has torn some muscle inside. We will get you downstairs and I will have a bit of a probe about." Debbie was the nurse who drew the short straw. She poured the anesthetic on the wound as directed and then, after a moment or two started to take out the clips. These clips are really like a carpenters steel staples put in with a staple gun. I have to tell you, as I told everyone who was within a four-penny bus ride of my bedside, that the local anesthetic did not work. Did, it not work. From the first twist of the removal tool, I let out a yell, and the politest expletive I good think of, even though I had already used it once when quietly discussing acupuncture with Doctor Meong Liu (or was it Liu Meong), was "BLOODY ADA".

"Sorry Basil" said Debbie, who really was and would have preferred to be anywhere, even down at the zoo mucking out the elephants, than pulling metal hooks out of tender skin. She took out two more. The sweat on my brow was equalled only by the sweat on hers. She went to get Sue, who today was the sister in charge. Sue had a look, and the wound was clearly bleeding from where the staples were being removed.   Sue broke open another phial of anesthetic.   "We should be injecting this" she said, to no-one in-particular.

"Mr Breading said pour it in the wound" replied Debbie.   They tried another couple of staples and then Sue said.   "That's enough, we'll take him down and tell Mr Breading its causing too much discomfort."

If that's discomfort, I thought, I wonder what 'pain' feels like?

Sue turned to me. "OK Basil, you've had enough of that, I expect Mr Breading will inject you before he takes any more out."   Mr Breading didn't, but in fairness, neither did he do much probing.   After a minute or two of gentle examination he said to me.

"Well old chap, I think we'll get you back down into surgery tomorrow, open you up and have a proper look at the problem."   Personally I suspected that once they opened me up they would find a Swiss army knife, a ball of string, and, possibly, even an irate car park attendant.

Battered and worn, they took me back to my room.   Polly arrived soon afterwards.   I felt as if I had been kicked around a football field.   She was there when they gave me Tramadol, she was there when, I turned grey, she was there when I was sick, she was there when I broke out in a cold clammy sweat.   She was there when I was engulfed by a headache that rates amongst the worst I have ever experienced.   I felt so poorly I had to ask her to go so that I could die in peace. That night was the longest of my life. I couldn't sleep, I felt desperately ill, and watched the big hand as it crept its way past the morning hours. I thought the dicky birds would never bring the dawn. Even the Tigers were more fun than this. At last, the dawn chorus began and the nurse brought me a cup of tea that I wasn't allowed to drink. At 8.30 the anaesthetist prepared me for surgery, at 9.0 o'clock I was wheeled into the theatre.

It was 11 o'clock and I awoke back in my room. Although I felt a little woozy, I knew somehow that my nights problems were behind me. From that moment on my recovery was assured. By lunchtime I was hungry, They wouldn't let me have anything, but I did have a cup of tea and a biscuit mid-afternoon. Polly came and we did crosswords and played dominos. Polly left about 7 o'clock and I slept like a baby until they brought me a cup of tea at 6.30 the next morning. I felt no pain, no nausea. There was no blood and gore on either my nightie or the sheets Mr Breading called in a 7.30 and said I could have breakfast. I had grapefruit followed by scrambled egg. For lunch I had grilled salmon, in the evening a mushroom omelette. The next day they let me go home. In the ten days I had been in the hospital I had grown very attached to the nurses and to Dr. Kim. How do they stay so cheerful all of the time. Dr Kim and Sonika, both missed their native South Africa so much and told me so much about it, that, under my new *'make the most of''* life style policies I was determined to take the Blue Train, that wonderfully luxurious train journey from Pretoria to Port Elizabeth. Polly and I discussed it at length and made a definite commitment to book it for our 40th wedding anniversary in March 2005. Nonetheless. I said goodbye to them without regret at my going, although, it must be said, I will always remember with feelings akin to love, Dr Kim, Sonika, Sue, Debbie, Patsy, Alison, Jo and all the other wonderful nurses who, far from turning a drama into a crisis removed any opportunity for self-pity and made me realize, without a doubt and for evermore that even a painful experience has a funny side - *even if it is prune shaped.*

As it happened I was destined to see one or two of them again, but that was still a little in the future. For now, my sojourn in Winterlands was over. I took away with me some good moments, some painful moments, some happy memories, some bloated episodes and a tube up my little black and blue friend.

CHAPTER 19
NEVER GET TOO CLOSE TO A
NEW MOTHER WITH A COUGH

OCTOBER/DECEMBER 2004

The family had come to see me for the week-end.   Tania and Nigel (and of course Jack they wouldn't have been let in without him) came on Euro-Star from Paris.   Tim and Virve, live in Sevenoaks, and that is only just around the corner, Jem flew in from Tenerife and collected Steph, who came to see me in Hospital and then was persuaded to stay for the week-end.   I wanted to invite mum, but she still thought I was in my deck chair in Tenerife, and although we could have done the great and late disclosure, I was still sleeping for great chunks of the day, and walking as if I was a hundred and two years old.   This was only due in part to the wound, but in greater part to the catheter and still unfamiliar leg bag.

We had a very gentle week-end. The children had the odd pub sortie, but Anne and I didn't join them.   We had three evening meals at home, one cooked by Polly, one cooked by son-in-law Nigel, and the third cooked by a Chinese lady from the Chopsticks and Bowl.

The district nurse came in on Saturday to change my dressing.   She asked if I had any questions. I did, and it was a big one spurred on by the memory of half a dozen 'bladder flushes' the joy of which was still still engraved in my mind.

"What happens?", I asked "If I get a blood clot blocking the catheter"

"Your bladder will fill up" she said, and then, before I could respond she smiled, "I know what you mean and frankly, the best and the quickest solution would be to get your wife to drive you to Winterlands, the nurse's are on duty 24 hours a day, and as a patient just discharged, you will get absolute priority".

"OK" I said.

"Word of advice" she said.   "Don't wait until you are in agony.   If the bag is not filling, get yourself along there in good time"

"I hope it wont be necessary" I said.

"So, do I" said the nurse, "but don't bank on it, there will still be a bit of bleeding, so small clots are not unusual."   Her words were to prove prophetic over the next ten days.

The children all went back to their homes, and Polly and I started a routine of rising at about 9 o'clock, pottering around the house until about mid-day.   Taking a ride in the local countryside and stopping off somewhere for lunch.   Returning to the house around 2 o'clock, when I would go to bed and sleep until about 4 o'clock. We would then spend a quiet evening, and go to bed around 9.30 or 10.

I was, as I had been told, convalescing whilst waiting for the 2nd of November when three things were due to happen.

1. My stitches would be removed.
2. My catheter would become a terrible dream.
3. Mr Breading would say. "Good News, your lymph nodes were clear"

As the time progressed we began to think about the future. Now, it was easier to believe there was one, and one which hopefully could become, as the song said, a long and winding road. In March 2005 we would have been married for 40 years. We had already half decided that the Blue Train would be a special way to mark our ruby day. After all, had I not more or less promised Dr. Kim and Nurse Sonika, that that is what we would do. So with our new adventurous spirit decided, we confirmed it and booked the Blue Train as part of a 16 day tour of South Africa, incorporating a safari, a visit to Victoria Falls, and a trip up Table Mountain. We did our best to coincide the actual wedding anniversary date of March 20th with an overnight on the train as it rumbled its way across that huge continent.

Continuing this new adventurous life-style, we visited Polly's brother John the day following and had lunch at the Beau Rivage in Tankerton, and began to 'fill' the time until our return to Tenerife in November.

The nurse paid me regular visits, pleased with my progress. We returned to the Limetree to taunt John with the success of the operation, and confirm that, on this occasion, Basil was NOT one in a hundred. By this time he had realized the insensitivity of his chat just hours before I was to be wheeled into Theatre. I held nothing against him before, and even less after he insisted on giving me a Kir Royale on the house.

The first mini crisis occurred on the Friday, with just four days to go to catheter removal time. A blood clot cut off the flow. We gave it a couple of hours, and then Polly drove me to Winterlands. Reception phoned upstairs to the Lister Ward, and the Ward Clerk came down to get me.

"I've told them you're here" she said, and Dr Kim would like to deal with you herself." She showed me into Room 14. I didn't get on the bed, but stood looking out of the window.

"Basil" a voice said. "You're much taller lying down." I turned around, Dr Kim was standing leaning against the door post.

"Does that mean you don't want to marry me?" I asked

"It's just a surprise" she said "I've never seen you standing up." I'm waiting for the day, I thought, I sighed.

"I expect you want me to take my trousers off?"

"Well, it will be easier than fiddling about up your trouser leg". I took my trousers off and went to get on the bed.

"Take your shirt off as well, she said and I'll have a look at the wound."

"Can I keep my socks on?" I asked

"Don't all men" she said. I lay on the bed. "Would you like a gown?", she said, busy fiddling with my 'little friend,' who I was delighted to say was no longer black and blue, although still decidedly 'little.'

"No," I answered, "but if my wife comes in just pretend you're a doctor." She smiled and shook her head, clearly giving me less than full marks for originality. We went through the procedure that I had become accustomed to. It seemed less painful than it used to, and Kim's biceps had clearly expanded into the job.

"When does the catheter come out?" she asked.

"Tuesday", I said.

"Then you will be able to find out if everything works" she said

"What do you think?" I said, "as a doctor" I added.

"Well, the incontinence shouldn't be a problem. You may find it a bit difficult for a few days when you cough, or stand up, but as long as you keep doing your pelvic floor exercises it will soon pass."

"That's good to hear" I said.

"The impotence" she paused "Can't tell, every man who has this operation is affected to some degree. You will just have to wait and see. Mr Breading will have told you about Viagra, and there are also mechanical aids. For now, don't worry about it, in the worst cases there is even a surgical procedure which helps." Dr Kim was a girl of quiet dedication, long hours, and one-liners. This was the longest serious speech she had delivered. I smiled at her.

"Thank you for that" I said, seriously grateful, "You know, I could develop a real soft spot for you."

"For some time to come" she smiled, "a 'soft spot' is the best you will develop for anyone."

She re-dressed the wound, helped me off the bed and left me to get ready. When she came back, I said.

"We've booked the Blue Train"

"Good for you" she said, "I am sure you will enjoy it. "Now, off you go, and the best of luck on the 2nd."

As we got closer to the 2nd, and the big three. Stitches, Catheter and All Clear (I refused to believe that there would be any other result) The days dragged a little. In the event, I was not going to have to wait until the Tuesday for the catheter to be removed. Tim, came to see me on Monday morning, to discuss a few business ideas. He arrived around 11 o'clock. We were going to join Polly at the golf club for lunch at around 12.30.

She had gone off to play golf at 9.30. By 11.30, it was clear that I had another blood clot. I had to ask Tim to take me to Winterlands. He did, and I was shown immediately up to room 14. Debbie came to see me, but not to do the bladder flush. Sue came to see me, but not to do the bladder flush. Dr Kim came in. "When do you get rid of that thing?" she said nodding her head to a point just below my belly button. I followed her gaze.

"I hope you mean the catheter" I said

"I mean the catheter" she answered.

"Tomorrow morning" I said if everything goes according to plan.

"I think I will telephone Mr Breading and see if we can get rid of it for you now."

"The catheter?" I queried

"The catheter" she agreed.

She phoned the great man, he agreed, and my cup runneth over even if my leg bag didn't.

"OK" said Dr Kim, "We can take it out now, Sue will do it for you." My relief was obvious.

"That's great I said, I'm meeting Polly at the golf club for lunch." She looked at her watch.

"Not a chance" she said, you will be sitting quietly in that chair for the next two or three hours, until you show us that you can wee on your own."

"Oh, dear" I said, "my son is sitting in the car park waiting for me, to take me to the golf club."

"I'll go and tell him" said Dr Kim, "he and his mum can have a quiet lunch on their own. You should be ready by about three o'clock." Sue injected a mild anesthetic down the tube and waited for it to take effect. That's to stop the pain as I pull the tube out" she said "we don't do pain in Winterlands." It was nice to see her cheerful countenance again, particularly when she said. "As you are our guest again, I better go and get you the lunch menu whilst that little lot numbs your feelings." She came back with the menu. In keeping with my new rigid diet routine I ordered just smoked salmon and scrambled egg, then watched as the tube was withdrawn.

I sat in the chair, Sue went of duty, Polly arrived about 2.30. Sonika came on duty. We talked about the Blue Train, then she told me I couldn't go home until I wee'd 200 mil in one go. I eventually left after five hours. But I left without the bag.

That evening, and early morning, I found coughing containable, but the need to clench very hard when standing up. I practiced my pelvic floor exercises assiduously, and could feel the constant improvement. At 9.40 I was sitting in the Winterlands reception (again). At 9.45 I was lying on a couch in the treatment room having been greeted by a very smiley Mr Breading, who's face, despite it's cheerfulness, had given away nothing. He had left me to the tender mercies of the nurse who then prepared me. When he returned, Polly was sitting in the corner shielded by the curtain. "Well Basil," he said. "You're clear of cancer." Just like that, no fanfare, no rapturous applause just. "Well Basil, you're clear of cancer"

"The lymph nodes were clear?" I asked.

"completely" he said. He looked at the wound. "That's fine, the nurse will remove the stitches and you can go. I want to see you in about a month." We settled for the 22nd December. Go to your GP and get a PSA test and bring it along with you." He smiled, patted my arm and prepared to leave.

"Is the final blood test routine?" I said.

"Well, you could call it the final hurdle" he said. "I would expect your PSA to be no more that 0.4."

"And if it's not?" I asked.

"That's a bridge we cross if and when" he replied

On the way out he spotted Polly. "You heard all that?" he said,

"Yes" I heard her reply, "He does have a bit of back ache at the moment."

"Nothing to do with the operation" he said. And was gone.

"Thank you Mr Breading" I murmured.

I phoned all the children and gave them the news. The next morning I went to see the lovely Nita. She already knew, and appeared very pleased that her timely intervention had had such a successful outcome. "How's the incontinence?",

"I'm getting to grips" I said, particularly with the pelvic floor exercises

"Welcome to the wonderful world of women" she said, "there's a saying. never get to close to a new mother with a cough." She laughed outrageously. I joined in. "How's the impotence?" I grimaced "Have you tried yet", I grimaced again. "You qualify for Viagra after a Radical Prostatectomy. I'll start you on 50 mil. I am allowed to give you a whole months supply." I perked up, she paused. "FOUR TABLETS" don't waste them, If one does not work, you can take 100 mil. That's two tablets"

"It's also two times" I said - "in a whole month" I said "talk about rationing" She said nothing, but had the grace to smile. "You're off to Tenerife tomorrow" she reminded me, just relax in the sun shine, take it slowly, and the warmth, the relaxation and the Viagra should do the trick."

"Is there anything else I should know?" I asked, wondering if there was anything else I should know.

"There are side effects" she said, "but the only one you really need to worry about is a prolonged erection." Her eyes twinkled. "This could last up to six hours, its rare, and will need hospital attention. Don't risk it if your about to go out for a game of Tennis."

She got serious. "Basil, I really am delighted I insisted on the PSA test. You had no symptoms, the cancer was high grade, another six months, you *would* have had symptoms, but by that time the cancer would certainly have spread." I took her hand.

"Goodbye Nita" I said, " I owe you a life."

CHAPTER 20
EVERYWHERE EXCEPT
SAINSBURY'S

NOVEMBER 2004 TO APRIL 2005

This chapter is really just a 'mopping up' exercise, and not particularly in the incontinence sense. When I left 'The Lovely Nita" there were three issues unresolved.

1. Would my PSA in December be below the required 0.4 or did I still have a problem? *(you remember the book - in 3 out of 4 men the cancer has already spread)*

2. Will I be comfortable daily sailing my boat over the lake of incontinence?

3. Will 4 Viagra a month be enough - or will they be too many?

Read on my friends.

In the main it is fair to say that I left the tigers behind me in Winterlands. In truth they still visited me from time to time in the darkest hours of the night when the world is still and the mind

is not.   They would remind me of the words in
PROSTATE CANCER - QUESTIONS AND ANSWERS.

*'**FEAR**' Could in fact quote verbatim from Page 16 -* *'THREE TO FOUR OUT OF TEN MEN WILL FIND THAT THE CANCER HAD SPREAD EVEN DESPITE THE OPERATION.'* *He would remind me of Mr Breading's dismissive words when I asked what happened if my PSA gave a reading above 0.4 when I saw him in December.* *"WE WILL CROSS THAT BRIDGE **IF/WHEN** WE COME TO IT"*
When he was in a really mischievous mood he would tell me that *"ONCE YOU HAVE HAD CANCER IT IS ALWAYS LURKING, JUST WAITING TO REAR ITS UGLY HEAD AGAIN AT THE DROP OF A HAT"*

My other tigers still played their defensive part *'**HOPE**' constantly reminded me that the operation had been a great success.*

*'**RESIGNATION**' just kept telling me that all that could be done, had been done, and just to wait until December 22nd and my next PSA test.*

*My most frequent visitor, strangely enough, was '**REGRET**'. He became a real bore.   "WHY OH WHY,?" he would say "DID YOU HAVE TO RUSH TO GO UNDER THE KNIFE.   WHY DIDN'T YOU REALLY EXAMINE THE OPTIONS.   IF YOU HAD HAD CHEMO OR RADIOTHERAPY, WHAT'S LEFT OF YOUR HAIR MIGHT HAVE FALLEN OUT, BUT AT LEAST YOU WOULD STILL BE ABLE TO STAND-UP FOR YOURSELF?" I listened hard to what he had to say in those pre-dawn hours. He talked incessantly about living with the results of a Radical Prostatectomy. He talked about the incontinence which thankfully* *had been relatively short-lived and relatively easy to overcome. True to say that even now, a violent coughing spell, a gargantuan sneeze or an episode of Black Adder could put me in slight danger - as could the need to extricate myself from tight places, bungee jumping, wing walking or a shanked pitching wedge 50 yards from the flag. These occasional living inconveniences I could accept with gratitude, particularly when I reminded myself of the ultimate alternative that faced me. However, it is true to say in those dark lonely hours I would wonder if I had risked this slight lessening of the quality of my life, not wholly because I was nervous that the alternative treatments offered, tended, in the end, to simply delay the inevitable, but partly because I did not want to spend the winter in England taking weekly treks to the hospital, when I could be lazing in the sunshine of Tenerife. Always, however, those doubts vanished with the sun.*

It must be said that daily the incontinence problem had eased. The pelvic floor exercises so close to every new mothers *heart?* are a lot easier to cope with than an hour in the gym, and within a week or two it was only at moments of extreme pressure - like a 6 foot putt to halve the hole - that I had to remember the good old buttock clench.

The greater problem, as I had indicated to the lovely Nita, was the impotence. It was severe, *but was it permanent?* In all the best circles they no longer call that sad inability *'Impotence'* it is known by the far more politically correct tag of *E.D.* or *'Erectile Dysfunction'*   It means that at a cocktail party in the best of society, you can sip your martini, curl your finger around a Beluga and Ketchup Vol-au-Vent, and join in a medical conversation with "Yes old boy, I've been diagnosed with a touch of the old E.D. don't you know. Of course, I'm under the doctor" and under the doctor, in the nicest possible way,   indeed I was.

The day before we were due to leave for Tenerife I faced up to the need for a little strategic planning, something which has never been my strong point.   Now, in the 63rd year of my life, I was faced with a bit of the old S.P. that would have made Napoleon's winter march through Russia seem like child's play.   I had FOUR Viagra tablets, a large appetite, a reluctant appendage, and almost 3 months in Tenerife. Mr Breading had mentioned 'Mechanical Aids' in our little talk, and so I thought that perhaps a back-up to the Viagra, namely one of these before mentioned mechanical aids, might be appropriate.   He had not described this item in any detail, but being a man of the world I had heard what some men have done with vacuum cleaner nozzles and assumed it was something on those lines.   I looked up 'Adult Shops' in yellow pages and found one in the nearby naval town of Chatham *(all the nice girls love a sailor)* so it appeared on the face of it to be an appropriate base for its purpose.   Polly and I had been for a drive one day.   We had enjoyed a civilised lunch in an oak beamed hostelry and, by mid afternoon I had contrived to end up in the vicinity of this splendid metropolis.   Nonchalantly I said, "Ah, Chatham" implying, of course, *goodness me, fancy us ending up here, what a surprise.*   "Tell you what, as we're here, I would like to call into a shop I have heard about in Chatham."

"What for?" said Polly,

"Oh, just for something, I've heard about, to help me get over the operation" I said

"What's that?" she said.   Why is life also so difficult I thought

"Oh just.......an aid" I said, pleased as punch with the word.

"An aid to what?" she said.   It was no good, full discussion was inevitable.

"Well, you remember when you were sitting behind the curtain at Mr Breading's last consultation."

"Yessssss"

"And Mr Breading talked about mechanical aids"

"Yeessssss"

"Well, I've done a bit of research, and this shop, well it stocks medical aids like that"

"Like what?"

"You know"

"Do I?" but she was smiling.   "Go on then" she said.

I parked the car, I even put £1 coin in the pay and display, and I walked across the road and into the discreetly positioned shop which modestly proclaimed in flashing neon lights **"ADULT SHOP - PRIVATE CABINS AVAILABLE"**

A quiet bell jangled loudly as I opened the door and I was reminded of the last time I had had occasion to go into such an establishment.

It was about 1980 and I would have been in my late 30's. I was a founder member of an Old Tyme Music Hall Society, called appropriately BOTMS, and we were looking for a rubber doll to be portrayed as a trapeze artiste in one of our sketches, we even had this idea of pulling her plug and letting her whirl around the stage blowing raspberries like the old party favourite, the deflating balloon.

"I know some shops in Soho that sell rubber dollies" said one of our company who just happened to know some shops in Soho that sold rubber dollies. "I'll pop in when I'm in town next week," then, as an afterthought, he added "if anybody happens to be in town next week I'd, well, I'd welcome the company." I was going to be in London next week, like I was in fact every week, and so I became a willing volunteer, believing I would gain far more than I lost. How wrong can one be and still be a member of the Brownies.

We agreed to go on Tuesday lunch time and were meeting for lunch at a small restaurant just off Leicester Square. I was working in Mayfair at the time and it was no hardship for me. Mobile phones had been invented but were not in common use. I certainly did not have one. I arrived in the small eatery in good time, and sat there alone and ignored. My friend simply did not turn up. He later explained that he had 'phoned my office just after I had left to explain that he had an appointment which was going to make it impossible to get there. As the big hand approached the 12 and the little hand the 2, I decided that I would have to carry out this potentially embarrassing mission on my own.

A quiet bell jangled loudly as I opened the door *(notice the clever link)*. So far so good. All around the walls were book racks filled with .... books. Strangely, and most unlike the local library or WH Smiths, they did not expose the spine of the book but the front cover. They appeared to be mainly medical books - particularly on subjects anatomical, and even perhaps gynaecological. Alright, even at 38 I wasn't that naive - I knew exactly what they were. But I was there on a mission, and so I only browsed for an hour or two before focusing my attention on the subject of my visit. A rubber dolly. Everything was quietly low key. Men in grubby Macs *(although some had bowler hats)* thumbed through back issues as if they were studying form in the racing post. Ladies were conspicuous by their absence, EXCEPT that is, for a blousy blonde behind the counter. A man of Latin origin (possibly) was busy stocking shelves.

I looked around the walls, there suspended from the ceiling were a full range of rubber dollies. Black, Bronze, and White. Blondes, Brunettes and Redheads.

Many of them (probably all of them) were hanging there open mouthed in surprise, obviously at the indignity being heaped upon them. Behind this aerial display, high on an un-reachable shelf, were the boxes from which these flying beauties had emerged. Very colourful, most explicit, and, it had to be said, bearing little resemblance to their rubber doppelgangers. They were all naked. What a surprise. I tried to imagine each one dressed in the sequined leotard that I was sure our wardrobe mistress Madam Audrey would provide. I tried to imagine this sequin clad lady standing astride the shoulders of the most athletic of our young cast as the apex of the human pyramid that was to be the finale of our ambitious circus scene. After much contemplation I decided to settle for the little blonde with the pony tail and a mouth showing slightly less open surprise than her companions. I sidled up to the 'not so little' blonde behind the counter. *"Excuse me"* I said in a bumpkin up from the country sort of a voice. *"I'm interested in the little blonde doll with the pony tail"*

"What's that luv" said the blousy blonde in a loud brassy voice that matched her make up.

"The blonde doll with the pony tail" I almost whispered, Blousy gave me a sly smile, she winked,

and before I could finish my sentence called out to the Latin man in a voice that could shatter glass.

"Miko, bloke here got a yen for Juicy Lucy, bring her over so 'ee can have good look, there's a duck."

"Where?" I wanted to say, but with every grubby Mac and bowler hat now facing in my direction, I quietly, as is the way of the very best 'News of the World' reporters, made my excuses and left.

I had failed, but clearly I could not go home empty handed.   Three shops later I was able to find a shelf of reachable height, help myself to a box, hurry to the counter and pay cash without a word being spoken.

Although I told my story colourfully at the next rehearsal of BOTMS, the girls were not impressed when I unpacked the box to reveal a hugely bossomed lady with the most surprised look on the planet.   To make it worst she appeared to be bald.   The saga of the rubber doll followed me un-relentingly, and was recalled for many years both on-stage and off.

But I digress.   At this much later time, a far older and slightly wiser man listened to the quiet bell that jangled loudly, and entered the shop on quite a different mission.   I stood and took stock.   Videos and DVD's on one wall, books on a second wall.   Posters and a doorway through to very discreet *'Private Cabins'* on a third, and there at the end, a wide array of mechanical aids to suit every pocket and for every purpose you could imagine - and a great number you couldn't. It was the work of a moment to scan the shelves, find a box the picture on which more or less depicted the sort of function I had in mind, ignore the warning that stated *'This product is for NOVELTY only and is NOT a medical aid'* part with sixty something pounds *(some NOVELTY this was going to be),* and rejoin Polly in the car with barely 2 pence of my £1 parking fee used.

"You got it?" she said

"I got it" I answered. There was no more to be said.

To make it work you would have needed hands like the Big Friendly Giant and muscles like Arnold Schwarzenegger. but we didn't find **that** out until almost three minutes after we arrived home. I put it back in the box and filed it in the dustbin.

"Make sure its well hidden" said Polly. I tucked it under a week old copy of the Financial Times with a philosophical aside to Polly, "well, so much for our sixty pound experiment"

"Our" she queried in a raising the eyebrows sort of voice. I didn't pursue the matter. Nil Desperandum, I still had four Viagra Tablets. With a bit of luck one of them would give me the prolonged erection that required hospital treatment.

I was determined to practice restraint, and so I didn't take my first Viagra until *after* the plane had landed in Tenerife. The first one didn't work..... twice. I took two. They didn't work three times. I kept the fourth as a souvenir. My mother always told me, *"When things aren't going your way, make do and mend"* I never knew quite what it meant, but for the remainder of our stay in Tenerife we simply made do and mended. We arrived back in England in mid December, and I immediately made an appointment with the lovely Nita to fulfil my promise and let her know how I had got on.

"Well Basil," she said, "how did you get on?"

"Unsuccessfully" I said

"Were you relaxed?" she said

"Yes" I said

"You tried properly?"

"Yes", I said on the verge of wondering whether I should be embarrassed

"Where?" she asked

"Everywhere but Sainsbury's" I said.

"What's wrong with Sainsbury's?" she wanted to know. No she didn't, I just made that up.

"You are joking" she did say.

"I am joking" I agreed, "It was Tesco's." She ignored me this time

"Oh well," she continued, "we must simply persevere." She got a book out of her desk, read it for a moment or two, and then turned to her computer. After a few moments she smiled, looked at me mischievously, and said "All is not lost, we can try you on Levitra, and if that fails there is another drug called Ciallis."

"Levitra, Ciallis", I said, "they sound like Latin American dance numbers",

" Well," she said, lets hope they give the two of you the chance to tango."

"As long as its not the Masochism Tango", I replied, remembering a splendid, if slightly irreverent Tom Lehrer song from the sixties. She simply raised an eyebrow, because, after all, at thirty-something years old you probably would never have heard of Tom Lehrer.

"Now, its only a day or so until you see Mr Breading. We have your PSA result and it is a wonderful 0.1, so there is no problem there, tell him about the Viagra, and see what he has to say. After that we can decide what to prescribe for you next." *A new black and blue friend would be nice, I thought,* but I said nothing except

"OK Nita, you're the boss."

With the good news about the PSA, I felt I had a whole evening to prepare for Mr Breading by carrying out a bit personal research into E.D. to add to what the lovely Nita had told me. On the Internet, I found a wealth of information. I tracked forward through Viagra to Levitra, and Ciallis and on to vacuum pumps. I recalled the filing cabinet into which I had consigned my Vacuum Pump and had decided not to waste any more time on pumps be they vacuum, submersible or even bicycle, when a single sentence caught my eye *"This is NOT a novelty but a serious medical aid recommended by the NHS."* I rushed to the dustbin, hoping to find the previously discarded

box. There it lay, *on top* of the Financial Times.
Oh dear, obviously either inquisitive cats, squirrels
or.....neighbours. Best not tell Polly. Emblazoned
on the side of the box were the words. *"This is a
NOVELTY and should not be used as a medical aid"*.
Now, I spotted that subtle difference in a flash.
I rushed back into the house, after once more
burying the box, and clicked onto the page. I liked
what I read. The essential difference appeared to
be that the NOVELTY was hand operated, hence
the vacuum was created by muscle power.   The
MEDICAL AID was battery driven which meant all
you had to do was lie back and think of England.
Within minutes, and at approximately three times
the price of my previous *Novelty,* I had ordered
one on-line.   Amazingly it arrived in a plain
package the next day, and I was trying it out even
before the postman had reached the end of the
garden path. Eureka. It worked. It was painful,
it made spontaneity a redundant experience, but
it worked.   Create a vacuum, with the aid of a
plastic tube of adequate proportions, switch on
the motor and in just a few moments it was like
old times.   Unfortunately there was a downside.
When the vacuum ceased to be, so did its splendid
results. However, this was easily, though painfully
overcome.   *"Just slip"* said the instructions,
*"one, or if necessary two of the silicon rubber
rings over the appliance, and when the vacuum
has done its job, before turning off the motor, slip
the rings off the appliance and onto the base of
the penis."*   This clearly prevented the blood that

had been encouraged into the appendage from rushing back down to your feet. These silicon rubber rings, I should add, must have been less than a tenth of the circumference of that which they were to encircle. The instruction went on *"It is important to remove the rings after about 30 minutes."* Well I have to say, I reckon they had added a naught to the instructions, but even three minutes was twice as long as the old days.

I decided, the pain was bearable from time to time, but certainly not several times a day for the rest of my life, and so I went back to the internet.

And there, I found the ultimate answer. A penile implant. I kid you not. A clever gadget is implanted down the internal length of the Penis. A clever little bag of tricks is concealed in the scrotum. Spontaneity at the squeeze of plastic bulb that fills the empty gadget with a special fluid. Game over, much later, another squeeze returns the special fluid back into the bag. Wow, that was for me. All other remedies I ignored.

December 22nd loomed, and Penile Implantment had to be the major item on my agenda for my upcoming consultation with Mr Breading.

The great man had started calling me Basil some time ago, nevertheless it was a good feeling when, on the day of my appointment, I was standing at reception when he breezed down the corridor.

"Morning Basil" he called "Hello Mrs Jay", you may as well come straight in." We followed him down the corridor and he opened the door for us whilst inviting us to sit down.

"I have my blood test result here" I said, waving the piece of paper that I had collected from the lovely Nita.

"And I have your blood test result here" he said waving a similar piece of paper." He smiled. "I had Georgina (his secretary) phone the surgery yesterday and ask them to fax a copy over."

"Are you happy with it?" I asked, confidently knowing the answer because the lovely Nita had told me.

"It's perfect" he said

"No bridges to cross then?" I asked, wondering if he would remember.

"No bridges to cross" he said, he remembered, "but" he added in a cautionary voice, "I will want to see you again in about three months, just to monitor progress."

"How are the other problems?" he asked. I was glad he had.

"Well", I said, folding my legs in a confidential manner, and leaning in towards him. "The incontinence, well, I've got that licked." The unfortunate turn of phrase did not even occur to me until his mouth turned up at the corners and he suddenly took a great interest on something on his blotting pad. I carried on regardless. "The impotence," I corrected myself, "The E.D. is another matter". I related my unsuccessful Viagra story, and told him about Nita's suggestion of either Levitra or Ciallis. I told him of the painful and therefore limited success of the vacuum pump (I neglected to mention the NOVELTY item that didn't work), and before he could respond, I plunged on. "Mr Breading," I said, dropping my voice to a confidential whisper. "I have been looking on the internet, and I would like to go for a penile transplant." *'TRANSPLANT' I cringed,* how **could** I have said that. I quickly, but not quickly enough, corrected myself, "*I mean a Penile IMPLANT*" I said in a small voice. He said nothing for a moment or two, and I suspect that he might have got something stuck in his throat. When he eventually looked up he appeared to be in complete control.

"Basil" he said looking at me in much the way that an infant teacher looks at a wayward child. "It is much to early for that. Your operation was only 3 months ago. The nerves have been damaged and they could take as much as a year to repair themselves - hopefully. Until then we have a whole raft of things we could try." He paused for breath and looked at me inviting a response. A disappointed

"Oh, I see" was all I could manage, then "What do you suggest we should try next?"

"Well", he said, steepling his fingers. "First lets try Levitra. If that doesn't work we will try Ciallis - they both work in different ways and it is quite likely that one of them will be successful."

"And if they're not?" I asked.

"Well, then we can go to an Asphrodial"

"An Asphrodial?" I said.

"It's a little pellet you push down the urethra with a special stick."   My eyes were already watering.   You can use this method as much as 7 or 8 times a week, and unlike the tablets it has very few side effects."   I was speechless so I said nothing.   "If that is unsuccessful we can move on to a daily injection directly into the penis."   I had heard enough, and put up my hands.

"I'm happy to start with the Levitra" I said "and lets see how we get on." Mr Breading however was not about to let go of the implant without another attempt to make me understand.

"I don't personal carry out penile implants" he said, "but I do have a colleague who does.   If it becomes necessary, and lets give it a full year first, I will pass you on to him" He paused, "but remember." once you have taken that step, you have looked over the brink."   I still haven't worked out what that means.

He shook my hand, and said "Have a good Christmas and winter in Tenerife, and I would like to see you in April."

"Thank you for all your advice" I said, and meant it.

It was back to see the lovely Nita.   "What did Mr Breading say?" she opened with.   I told her what Mr Breading had said.

"Fair enough," she said, "would you like to start with the Levitra or the Ciallis."

"It's as broad as it is long," I said, and then realised that it probably was.

"Alright", she said, "lets go with the Levitra. Like the Viagra, I can only give you 4 tablets."

"It is Christmas" I reminded her, and I am going to Tenerife for 12 weeks."

"Alright," she said, weakening, "but you will have to make a declaration."

"I declare," I said, "that its Christmas and I am going to Tenerife for 12 weeks."

"Not what I meant" she sighed, "but here you are, a prescription for 12 tablets - use them wisely, and same as before, try one, and if it doesn't work try two at a time....but no more." She smiled. I grimaced, I hadn't been rationed like this since the war, and I was only a toddler then.

I acted with great restraint, and frightened of the consequences did not take my first Levitra until the front door had closed behind us. It didn't work. The following day I tried two. They didn't work. I kept the other nine as souvenirs. One day I am going to have a hell of a party.

Twelve weeks is a long time in the sunshine with nothing to do but read a book, but remember, I had already been through it once when the Viagra hadn't worked, so I was able to take it in my stride, and, with a little improvisation we got by.

In mid March we were due to take a short holiday in South Africa. As we were flying from Heathrow to Johannesburg, we had to fly back to England first. We spent two days at home and this gave me the opportunity to rush in an see the lovely Nita. I wasted no time on small talk.

"One didn't work" I said, "neither did two."

"Where did you try?" she said, with what I detected was just a trace of voyeurism.   I felt we had been there before.

"Trust me" I said, "I know a Doctor" I continued, "so, what's next?"

She looked at her screen.   "It will have to be the Ciallis" she said

"When are you seeing Mr Breading again."

"Tuesday fortnight" I said, the day after we get back from South Africa, oh, and incidentally, he asked me to ask you to look at my PSA first"

"See the nurse on your way out" said Nita, "and we'll have the result ready for when you go to see him."   I saw the nurse on my way out, and the lovely Nita phoned me on my mobile as we were driving to Pretoria a few days later.

"Hi Basil" she said cheerily.   "It's Nita"

"You want me to come and see you?" I said,

"No need" she said, "your PSA shows at 0.1 which is absolutely perfect."

I breathed a sigh of relief, resisted a joke, and said simply

"Thank you Nita."

"You're welcome" she said "pop into reception and collect a print-out for Mr Breading as soon as you get back."

"I will" I said, "and thank you again, for everything."

"Don't forget to talk to him about the problem" she reminded me.   I didn't need reminding.

South Africa was a wonderful experience.   The Blue Train was sumptuous.   Table Mountain was very high, and quite flat. It looked a bit like a table. The garden route was a dream with places like Knysna and Pletenberg Bay being places you would happily spend your winters in. The Victoria Falls were awe inspiring. The game reserves in Botswana were stunning. THE CIALLIS DIDN'T WORK.

I went to see the lovely Nita the day after I returned, and the day before I went to see Mr Breading. I put on my sad face so that as I walked through the door she was able to say. "The Ciallis didn't work, did it?"

"No", I said, but it did give me a three day headache, and I do have two left to go with my spare Viagra and nine Levitra." What a cocktail they will make I thought.

"You see Mr Breading tomorrow.

"Yes"

"Here is your splendid PSA result - six months since the operation and still showing only 0.1"

"That's great news Nita, and thank you very much for phoning me with it.

"It's a shame we can't have the same success with the other problem" she said. "but don't despair, lets see what Mr Breading says tomorrow.

Mr Breading was delighted with PSA result and told me that, on that subject he didn't want to see me again until September. On the pressing matter of the ED he seemed disappointed, but not massively surprised that neither the Levitra or the

Ciallis had worked. "It's still only six months" he reminded me. "and all is not lost. We now move on to MUSE - this is the ALPROSTADIL TRANSURETHRAL we talked about on your last visit.. Lets give this a try at 500gm and if it doesn't work we can increase the dose to 1000 grm before needing to think about the injections.

"OK", I said, "what do I do?"

"When do you go back to Tenerife?"

"In three days, I said, "on Friday."

"OK" he said, "go to your doctor and get a prescription, bring it back to me on Friday when I have a clinic. What time do you have to be at the airport?"

"About 3.30" I said.

"Alright, come about 1.o'clock. You needn't make an appointment, just tell the receptionist to let me know you're here and I'll see you straight away."

"Thank you", I said, "but why am I coming?"

"Well these applicators are a bit tricky" he said, "and I want to show you how to use it." Feeling like a shuttlecock, I went back to the lovely Nita with the name of the drug written on a Winterland's compliment slip. She read it and said "I see, he didn't give you a prescription then?"

"No," I said, "he told me to get that from you." She appeared to be less than pleased. However, she printed me out a prescription. '*SINGLE DOSE APPLICATOR*' I read.

"Just one?" I asked

"Just one" she answered, they *are* £15 a go, and IF they work I can only give you 4 a month - you can of course have a private prescription" she added.

"At £15 a go it makes it a bit expensive" I said.

"Depends how many goes you want" - she smiled - the first of the session.

"Well, we could be looking at a grand a month" I smiled back.

"Not on a maximum ration of seven in any seven days." she said. I did the arithmetic. Seven times seven is forty-nine, forty-nine less four on the NHS is forty-four, forty four by £15 is almost £600. Perhaps I'll cut out Monday's.

"Thank you Nita", I said, "but there is just one more small thing."

"Another *small* thing" I imagined her saying, instead she cupped her chin in her hand, "Yesss" she said quietly.

"Before I went to Tenerife I bought, a proper Vacuum pump from an accredited NHS supplier on the internet......it was £150 + VAT" Nita frowned. I had printed out the page and showed her the section that said *"IN CERTAIN CIRCUMSTANCES THIS DEVISE IS AVAILABLE ON THE NHS"*

It went on to say *"OR IF FOR OWN USE WITHIN CERTAIN MEDICAL CATEGORIES YOU CAN CLAIM BACK THE VAT"*

Nita was quickly in with "If you have already bought one, why do you want another?"

"Oh Nita," I sighed, therein lies a tale.

"I would have thought nothing less of you" she said, "But I hope its fairly short, and medical."

"You know I have just been to South Africa." I began, settling back in my chair like a born raconteur.

"Yes," she said, sounding bored

"and Zimbabwe"

"and Botswana" she finished for me

"Yes, and you know how I fly backwards and forwards to Tenerife."

"I didn't know you flew backwards" she said wishing already that I was her next patient.

"Well", I ignored the comment "I carried my pump in my computer case as hand luggage." she raised her eyebrows, she could obviously guess what was coming.

"At the airport in Zimbabwe, I went through the X-ray machine, on the way back to Jo'berg" *(see how easily I can slip into native speak)* " when a black gentleman with an extremely big gun, asked me to empty my case. I did. There was no computer, the case is just an easy way to carry things. There were three pairs of black underpants, a screwed up T shirt" *Polly's face was a picture when she saw that* " two mobile phones, a calculator and….,"

"and a vacuum pump?" finished Nita

"You know that, and I know that" I said, "but my new black friend sadly, did not know that. He found only a plastic tube with a motor on the end, 5 silicon rubber rings, a tube of water-based lubricant and a couple of spare batteries, all together in a neat little carrying case."

"What this?" he said, holding the tube up in the air and looking at it from all angles.

"Ah," I said "that is a medical aid"

"What for?" he said, oblivious to the people piling up behind me.

"Last year I had an operation" I whispered "*a Radical Prostatechtomy*"

"What that?" he said

"An operation for cancer" I replied

"What this for?" he said, holding the tube up to the light again and waving it around.   How do you explain.   Particularly bearing in mind that, if only half the stories you hear about the anatomical differences of the races are true, my new black friend would never believe that this, by his standards, *slim* plastic tube was designed for the purpose for which you and I know it was intended.   Conscious of the queue gradually building up through the X-ray arch, and quite at a loss for words, I simply shrugged my shoulders, and said in a small voice *"Its just a medical aid to help me recover from my operation"*

"What you do with it?" my friend continued, and then, thankfully, either the light suddenly dawned, he got bored, or else he decided that he was not looking at a plastic component for a Gatling gun, because he pushed it untidily back into its case, and with a parting "You not bought in Zimbabwe?" told me to "move along then." I stuffed the other items back into my computer case and, as nonchalantly as possible strolled away, absolutely certain that behind me a dozen people, including my new black friend, were rolling around on the floor clutching their belly's to hold in the laughter. I paused, and looked Nita straight in the eye.

"So you see, Nita, I intend to leave one here and leave one in Tenerife, and if I go anywhere else, well, just make do and mend just like my mother taught me."

Without a word, but with a broad smile, she signed the VAT declaration and waved me out of the door. She nodded at the prescription for the single applicator of MUSE. "Have fun, and don't waste it" she said

"I won't," I said, but Mr Breading had other ideas.

"Did you get them Basil?" boomed Mr Breading as I walked into his room.

"Not them," I said, "just it"

"It?"

"Yes, it, the doctor would only prescribe one until I found out if it worked."

"That's a bit mean" he said,

"Particularly," I added as I am off to Tenerife today to collect my car. I wont be back for three weeks, and IF it works, I will have to wait until I get back to get any more."

"Oh well" he said, "can't be helped, slip your trousers off and sit in the edge of the couch and I will show you how to apply it." He showed me how to prepare myself and the applicator. He pointed out the small white capsule at the end of the applicator - a small plastic tube with a plunger on the end. He showed me how to carefully slide the tube down the urethra until it reached the hilt. He showed me how to depress the plunger, then carefully wiggle it around to make sure the capsule was safely dispatched. He showed me how to carefully withdraw the applicator and hold it up to ensure that the capsule was gone. The capsule WAS gone. Hey hold on, I only had one, and Mr Breading had discharged it there in his consulting room at 1 o'clock in the afternoon when I was about to got a catch a plane.

"There, he said, that was easy wasn't it?"

"It was my only one" I said

"Yes, a bit mean that" he said, "still, you needn't hang around, walk around a bit and it should start working within 10 or 15 minutes. If it doesn't do the trick give me a call and we can increase the dose to 1000 microgram."

"Thank you Mr Breading," I said, although half of me was saying something quite different.

Polly and the taxi were waiting for me outside the hospital. I joined her in the back seat "How did it go?" she said. I looked at her and then the ridiculousness of the situation hit me. Here I was, sitting in the back of a taxi on my way to catch a plane having just been injected with a drug that was designed to make me.....well, I don't need to paint a picture. I could not help but see the funny side as we set out for the airport and I told her what had happened. Needless to say, it didn't work, but perhaps the circumstances were not conducive. I was still laughing quietly as the plane left the runway and headed for our island of perpetual summer. After-all, we had got by for six months, on the basis of 'make do and mend' - I felt sure that another 3 weeks of creative improvisation was not going to be beyond the whit of man.

SIX MONTHS ON

The whit of man proved equal to the task. As week followed enthusiastic and imaginative week, natures self-healing powers began to assert themselves. It would be untrue to say that all is yet as it could be wished. But confidence runs high that the ultimate goal will be reached. The signs are good. The spectre of a implant (let alone a transplant) recedes by the day. For those men, who like me have trod the prostate path stay positive, as in any competitive sport, in times of trial you just have to practice a little more, a little harder, and a little more often - and there's not a lot wrong with that. You are here, you are alive, never forget the alternative that faced you such a short time ago. Don't be depressed, but keep this single positive thought in your mind. The day will arrive when, once again, you will be able to STAND UP FOR YOURSELF.

In moments of despair remember the presence of the most aggressive of all of our

Tigers.....FEAR, and invite him back into your pre-dawn waking. Let him remind you of the visits he made to you when your hope was at its lowest. When your future looked darker than the stormiest night. When you would have traded almost anything you had for the chance of another twenty, ten, or even five years of life. Your Tigers will always say the words you cannot say yourself. Listen to them, and remember.

WHEN THE TIGERS COME AT NIGHT - THEY COME AS YOUR FRIENDS.

Lightning Source UK Ltd.
Milton Keynes UK

177134UK00001B/29/A